The Supported Learning in Physics Project has received major support from

223083

Institute *of* **Physics**

2

ESSEX

Nuclear Electric

PHYSICS IN THE ENVIRONMENT

This unit was written by
Malcolm Parry and Richard Skelding

The project is also supported by
The Department for Education and
Employment

Heinemann

THE SUPPORTED LEARNING IN PHYSICS PROJECT

Management Group

Elizabeth Whitelegg, Project Director, The Open University

Professor Dick West, National Power Professor of Science Education, The Open University

Christopher Edwards, Project Coordinator, The Open University

Professor Mike Westbrook, Vice-President for Education, Industry and Public Affairs, The Institute of Physics

George Davies, Manager, College Recruitment, Ford of Britain

Geoff Abraham, Project Trialing Manager

Dorrie Giles, Director, Education and Professional Development, Institution of Electrical Engineers

Martin Tims, Manager, Education Programme, Esso UK

Catherine Wilson, Education Manager (Schools and Colleges), Institute of Physics

Production

This unit was written for the Project by Malcolm Parry, School of Education, Durham University, and Richard Skelding, Epic Multimedia Group, Brighton.

Other members of the production team for this unit were:

Elizabeth Whitelegg, Project Director and Academic Editor

Christopher Edwards, Project Coordinator

Andrew Coleman, Editor

John Coleman, Course Assessor

Alison George, Illustrator

Maureen Maybank, Unit Assessor

Julie Lynch, Project Secretary

Sian Lewis, Designer

Cartoons supplied by ABC Cartoons

COLEG LLANDRILLO COLLEGE LIBRARY RESOURCE CENTRE	
046119	
Greenhead	13.07.98
530PAR	£8.75

ISBN 0 435 68841 3

The Institute of Physics, 76 Portland Place, London, W1N 4AA.

First published 1998 by Heinemann Educational Publishers.

© 1998 The Institute of Physics.

All rights reserved. No part of this publication may be reproduced, stored in a retrieval system or transmitted, in any form or by any means, electrical, mechanical, photocopying, recording, or otherwise, without either the prior written permission of the publishers or a licence permitting restricted copying from the Copyright Licensing Agency Ltd, 90 Tottenham Court Road, London, W1P 9HE. This book may not be lent, resold, hired out or otherwise disposed of by way of trade in any form of binding or cover other than that in which it is published, without the prior consent of the publishers.

Printed in Spain by Edelvives.

For further information on the Supported Learning in Physics Project contact the Information and Marketing Officer, The Centre for Science Education, The Open University, Walton Hall, Milton Keynes, MK7 6AA.

1.1

COLEG LLANDRILLO COLLEGE
LIBRARY RESOURCE CENTRE
CANOLFAN ADNODDAU LLYFRGELL

CONTENTS

3

COLEG LLANDRILLO COLLEGE
LIBRARY RESOURCE CENTRE
CANOLFAN ADNODDAU LLYFRGELL

The SLIPP units introduce you to a new method of studying – one that you may not have used before. They will provide you with a way of studying on your own, or sometimes in small groups with other students in your class. Your teacher will be available to guide you in your use of this unit – giving you advice and help when they are needed and monitoring your progress – but mainly you will learn about this topic through your own study of this unit and the practical work associated with it.

We expect that you will study the unit during your normal physics lessons and also at other times – during free periods and homework sessions. Your teacher will give you guidance on how much time you need to spend on it. Your study will involve you in a variety of activities – you won't find yourself just reading the text, you will have to do some practical work (which we have called 'Explorations') and answer questions in the text as you go along. (Advice on how long each exploration is likely to take is given.) It is very important that you do answer the questions as you go along, rather than leaving them until you reach the end of a section (or indeed the end of the unit!), as they are there to help you to check whether you have understood the preceding text. If you find that you can't answer a question, then you should go over the relevant bit of text again. Some questions are followed immediately by their answers but you should resist the temptation to read the answer before you have thought about the question. If you find this difficult it may be a good idea to cover up the answer with a piece of paper while you think about the question. Other slightly longer or more demanding questions have their answers at the back of the section. You are likely to need help with these; this might be from a teacher or from working with other students.

It will be up to you to make notes on the physics you have learnt from this unit as you go along. You will need to use these notes to help you revise. You should also keep notes on how you arrived at your answers to the questions in the unit. It is important to show all your working out for each question and to set it out clearly, including the units at every stage. We try to do this in our answers to the questions in this unit.

Most sections start with a short 'Ready to Study' test. You should do this before reading any further to check that you have all the necessary knowledge to start the section. The answers for this test are also at the end of the section. If you have any difficulties with these questions, you should look back through your old GCSE notes to see if they can help you or discuss your difficulties with your teacher, who may decide to go over certain areas with you before you start the section or recommend a textbook that will help you.

The large number of practical explorations in the unit are designed to let you thoroughly immerse yourself in the topic and involve yourself in some real science. It is only after hands-on experiences that you really begin to think about and understand a situation. We suggest that you do some of these explorations with other students who are studying the unit and, when appropriate, present your results to the rest of the class. There are a large number of these explorations and it may not be possible for you to do all of them, so if everyone shares their results with others in the class you will all find out about some of the explorations that you are unable to do.

Your teacher will arrange times when the practical work can be undertaken. For health and safety reasons you must be properly supervised during laboratory sessions and your teacher will be responsible for running these sessions in accordance with your school's or college's normal health and safety procedures.

HEALTH AND SAFETY NOTE

The unit warns you about any potential hazards and suggests precautions whenever risk assessments are required of an employer under the Management of Health and Safety at Work Regulations 1992. We expect that employers will accept these precautions as forming the basis for risk assessments and as equivalent to those they normally advocate for school science. If teachers or technicians have any doubts, they should consult their employers.

However, in providing these warnings and suggestions, we make the assumption that practical work is conducted in a properly equipped and maintained laboratory and that field work takes account of any LEA or school or college guidelines on safe conduct. We also assume that care is taken with normal laboratory operations, such as heating and handling heavy objects, and that good laboratory practice is observed at all times.

Any mains-operated equipment should be properly maintained and the output from signal generators, amplifiers, etc., should not exceed 25 V rms.

No one needs telling that our environment is precious. Many people, especially the young, believe our environment is at risk from pollution, overpopulation and shortages of crucial resources: habitats are being damaged, perhaps irreparably; whole species have become extinct and continue to be lost; and research is now suggesting that pollution can affect the unborn child. The scale of the potential risk and the extent of the damage already sustained are open to debate, as are the policies that can remedy the situation. Some people, however, think that there is no problem because they believe Earth can repair itself, although whether this repair will include the perpetuation of human life is questioned. Other people believe that we must intervene using a variety of 'fixes', such as population control policies, legislation, financial incentives and penalties, and technology.

To assess any problem and its remedies requires sound knowledge and a sound perspective. This unit focuses on just two elements of the environmental debate: energy, especially the United Kingdom's position, and the effect of motor vehicles on the environment.

Energy is a pervasive topic, as you will know if you have studied any of the other SLIPP units. We are all consumers of energy, and energy use can influence our wealth, health and prosperity, the welfare of our environment and our neighbours, our climate and even our long-term survival.

The car has brought mobility and prosperity to many but at a great and increasing environmental cost.

To some physicists, energy is simply the currency of a useful accounting system, enabling them to assess, for example, a system's capacity to do work or the amount of thermal energy emitted by a system. Business people may view energy supply as a means of obtaining wealth. Political leaders have to be aware that the possession or lack of energy sources may lead to wars or acts of international vandalism. To uranium or coal miners, energy supply may be associated with jobs but also with misery and danger. Most people depend on an energy supply to some extent, and many of us take it for granted – until it is cut off.

Energy studies is topical and controversial – rarely a day passes without some mention in the media of an energy-related issue, whether it is climate change or pollution. Have a look at some recent newspapers to see what the latest energy-related articles are about.

The energy question is important globally and nationally, but it is also significant domestically. On the most superficial level, knowing about energy technology and economics can help us save money and live more comfortably at home, but more importantly it may also help us to live our lives in a way that safeguards the welfare of other people and even the planet. Because about half of energy consumption in a technological society such as ours is used in the home or for private transport, individuals like us can make a great difference.

There are no complete answers to many of the questions we will be posing in this unit, and there are often no right and wrong opinions on energy policy, just informed and uninformed ones. Studying the physics of energy will help us become better informed and better able to make choices.

We will be relying on general knowledge and common sense rather more in this unit than in the other SLIPP units – energy is such a pervasive concept that when studying it you will be able to apply things you have learnt in geography, history, economics, maths, chemistry, and design and technology, or by just keeping up with the news. So, do keep an eye on the media – TV, radio, science journals such as *New Scientist* and the newspapers. One advantage of studying energy from a physicist's point of view is that, in our subject, we are lucky to have a sensible and consistent set of units of measurement. While economists discuss tonnes of coal or oil equivalent, kilowatt hours, therms, cubic metres or even cubic feet of gas or British thermal units, we can simply stick to joules!

Section 2 looks first at the interrelation of world population, standards of living and energy use, then it focuses on the UK for a historical and economic perspective, and it ends with predictions of the lifetimes of fuels and policies for extending these. Section 3 explores the role conservation has to play in traditional electricity production, waste management and transport policy. Sections 4 and 5 focus on the impact of the car on the environment. Section 6 looks at solar energy and its interaction with Earth. Section 7 looks at how energy is absorbed and emitted by Earth. Section 8 looks at the technologies that can exploit solar energy. Section 9 is an energy audit, which teaches physics and life skills by asking you to perform an investigation on the energy used in your home. Section 10 concludes with a summary. Some of these topics are essential for some syllabuses, but not all; your teacher will advise you on the best route through the unit according to the syllabus you are following.

One last point; there is some dispute among scientists and teachers as to how to use the word 'heat'. Our view is that in an ideal world we are *heating* something when we *transfer thermal energy* to it. Strictly, we shouldn't talk of the heat *in* something, only the thermal energy in it (it is quite possible to be heating a gas while its thermal energy is falling – if it is doing mechanical work, for example, at the same time). Some writers think we should never use the word 'heat' as a noun, only as a verb: 'to heat' or 'heating'. While we try to stick to these 'rules' throughout this and the other SLIPP units, we occasionally use the word 'heat' in its everyday sense to avoid becoming too long-winded and pedantic.

In this section, we will be looking at some basic terms and definitions, we will see how valuable your work output is and why we use machines instead of slaves and servants! We will explore a little of the history of energy supply and examine the outlook for the future, for both the UK and the world, and try to explain why energy consumption has increased so much over the centuries.

READY TO STUDY TEST

Before you begin this section you should be able to:

■ convert 1 tonne (1 t) into kilograms

■ name and use SI prefixes correctly

■ list different forms of energy and their sources

■ define work, quote an equation to determine how much work is done and state the unit of work

■ define power, quote an equation for power and state its unit

■ calculate the efficiency of a system

■ write down the law of conservation of energy

■ describe the Bohr structure of the atom

■ recall and use the relationship between density, mass and volume

■ use the equation

    energy = Plank's constant × frequency, $E = hf$

    to work out the size of a quantum of energy carried by a photon

■ use the equation

    velocity = frequency × wavelength, $v = f\lambda$

    for waves

■ use the formulae for kinetic energy:

$$E_k = \frac{1}{2}mv^2$$

    and for gravitational potential energy:

$$E_{pot} = mgh$$

■ convert 1 kW h into joules.

QUESTIONS

R1 Explain what you understand by gravitational potential, kinetic, thermal and chemical energy.

R2 List as many different kinds of energy as you can.

R3 In which of the following circumstances is work done?
(a) A rocket accelerating from the launch pad.
(b) A rocket travelling through space at a steady velocity of $15\,000$ km h^{-1} remote from any planets or stars.
(c) A ski-tow hauling a skier up a ski slope.
(d) A skier going down the slope at a steady speed.
(e) A book resting on a table.

R4 A pump raises 2.00 t of wet cement 15.0 m in 50.0 s
(a) What is the weight of the wet cement?
(b) How much potential energy is gained in this time?
(c) How much work is done by the pump? (Ignore the kinetic energy gained by the wet cement.)
(d) How much output power does the pump develop?
(e) The pump draws 10.0 kW of electrical energy: how efficient is it? Give your answer both as a percentage and as a fraction between 0 and 1.
(f) If the pump works continually for an eight-hour shift, how many kW h will be consumed in this time? (Remember that 1 kW h is the energy 'consumed' by a one kilowatt device running for one hour.)

R5 Write down the law of conservation of energy.

R6 Draw a sketch of the Bohr model of the atom for helium, labelling the locations of its constituent parts, together with their relative masses and charges. You may place these in a table if you prefer.

R7 What is the mass of 4.0 litres of petrol? (Take the density of petrol to be 0.68×10^3 kg m^{-3} and remember that 1000 litre $= 1$ m^3.)

R8 Compare the kinetic energy of a bullet of mass 20 g travelling at 300 m s^{-1} with a 44 t lorry travelling at 80 km h^{-1}.

R9 A photon, a packet of light energy, has wavelength 550 nm. What is its frequency and energy? (The speed of light, $c = 3.0 \times 10^8$ m s^{-1} and Planck's constant, $h = 6.6 \times 10^{-34}$ J s.)

R10 How much potential energy does a 0.20 kg apple lose as it falls 5.0 m from a tree? (Use $g = 10$ N kg^{-1}.)

R11 Convert 1 kW h into joules

R12 Fill in the missing parts in Table 2.1.

Table 2.1

Prefix	Standard form	Symbol
	$\times 10^{12}$	T
	$\times 10^{9}$	
mega		
kilo		
	$\times 10^{2}$	
	$\times 10^{-1}$	d
centi		
		m
micro		
	$\times 10^{-9}$	n
pico		

2.1 Fundamentals and revision

What a physicist means by the word 'energy' tends to be rather different from what the world at large means. When people say someone is energetic they mean they are exuberant or powerful, or they do a lot of work in a short time. Some engineers mean 'electrical energy' when they use the word 'power'. People talk about energy running out, whereas we know that energy cannot be destroyed, just changed from one form to another. To a physicist, energy can exist in just two basic forms: kinetic and potential.

Kinetic energy is the energy possessed by a particle or body by virtue of its motion. **Potential energy** is the energy possessed by a particle or body by virtue of its position in a system, or by a system because of its state of stress.

 Try to indicate (don't explain) which of the energy forms in your list from R2 are potential and which are kinetic.

We will consider this in some detail below – correct your answer as we go along.

You are probably quite used to accepting that a moving vehicle has kinetic energy of $\frac{1}{2}mv^2$. A rotating system has kinetic energy too because all elements of it (except the infinitesimal bit lying on the axis of rotation) have their own share of kinetic energy, although the formula for calculating it is different.

If we treat **electromagnetic energy** as a stream of energetic particles called photons, these too may be considered to have kinetic energy. As you can imagine, energies in one photon are pretty small, even for punch-packing gamma-rays. This doesn't mean that they are harmless though!

The broader category of potential energy is not quite as straightforward. An apple in a tree has potential energy because it is experiencing the gravitational force of Earth acting on its mass (resulting in its weight), which is balanced by the pull of the tree. If it drops from the tree it will experience a resultant force that will accelerate it and it will gain kinetic energy. When it lies on the ground, it still has potential energy – because it is still immersed in Earth's gravitational field – and it still experiences balanced forces, but each is a little less than before. We could 'extract' more energy from the system by digging a hole under it and letting it fall some more. We assign the position of zero potential energy quite arbitrarily, on the basis of convenience: sometimes at ground level, sometimes at infinity, sometimes elsewhere.

Strain (or elastic) energy exists because of the forces that hold molecules together. These are electrostatic in origin: neighbouring atoms exert forces on each other that are attractive when the atoms are separated and repulsive when they are too close. So, strain energy is a form of potential energy too (as is electrostatic energy). Strain energy in a spring is determined from

$$E_{strain} = \frac{1}{2}kx^2$$

where k, the spring constant, is a measure of stiffness: i.e. how much force per unit length of contraction or extension, x, must be applied to compress or extend the spring.

Sounds are caused by vibrations and are therefore associated with both kinetic and potential energy in exchange. For mechanical oscillations, the power, P, in a wave is proportional to frequency squared and amplitude squared.

Q1   After a petrol price rise, an inventor tries to build a full-sized wind-up car. The car contains a compression spring engine of stiffness $k = 2.0 \times 10^5$ N m^{-1}; how much does it extend when used to accelerate the car up to 50 km h^{-1}? The mass of the car is 1.5 t. ◆

Charges in a cell or battery have potential energy. As charge q leaves the cell it takes with it energy qV, where V is the potential difference across the cell's terminals. The charge does **work** equal to this quantity as it travels around the circuit. The amount of charge leaving a cell in time t is It, where I is the current in amperes. A charge accelerated (down a TV tube, for example) has, of course, got kinetic energy.

 A dry cell delivers 0.80 A to a circuit at 1.5 V for 2.0 h. How much (a) charge and (b) energy leaves the cell in this time?

(a)

$q = It$

$= 0.80\,\text{A} \times 2.0 \times 3600\,\text{s}$

$= 5760\,\text{C}$

$= 5.8 \times 10^3\,\text{C}$ (to two significant figures)

(b)

$E = qV$

$= 5760\,\text{C} \times 1.5\,\text{V}$

$= 8640\,\text{J}$

$= 8.6 \times 10^3\,\text{J}$ (to two significant figures)

 How fast does an electron travel when accelerated from rest through a potential difference of 5.0 kV. (Take the mass of the electron to be 9.1×10^{-31} kg and the charge on the electron to be 1.6×10^{-19} C.)

By definition

$$\text{potential difference} = \frac{\text{energy gained}}{\text{charge}}$$

therefore

kinetic energy gained by electron = potential difference × charge

so

$E_k = 5000\,\text{V} \times 1.6 \times 10^{-19}\,\text{C}$

$= 8 \times 10^{-16}\,\text{J}$

Since

$E_k = \frac{1}{2}mv^2$

$$v^2 = \frac{2 \times 8.0 \times 10^{-16}\,\text{J}}{9.1 \times 10^{-31}\,\text{kg}}$$

$$= 1.76 \times 10^{15}\,\text{m}^2\,\text{s}^{-2}$$

and

$$v = 4.2 \times 10^7\,\text{ms}^{-1} \text{ (to two significant figures)}$$

Thermal energy, or rather **internal energy** in solids and liquids, is associated with molecular vibrations. In common with mechanical oscillators, the molecules have a mixture of potential and kinetic energy that is constantly being exchanged. The potential energy arises because each molecule or atom interacts with its neighbours. In gases, significant intermolecular attraction exists only during collisions. For most of the time, gas molecules' energy is simply kinetic. All but the simplest molecules have both rotational and linear (or translational) kinetic energy. How does energy leave or enter such a system? Either through mechanical interactions with other molecules or through photons. When a photon is emitted, the energy of a molecule or atom falls, when a photon is absorbed, the energy of the molecule or atom rises. Depending on how big or small the transition is, high-energy or low-energy photons are involved. Most thermal energy emission by molecules is infrared, but at high temperatures significant numbers of visible and ultraviolet photons can be emitted by matter.

Radioactive (nuclear) energy is kinetic energy in the form of moving particles or photons emitted by unstable nuclei.

To understand some forms of energy, and what fuels are, we must think about **equilibrium** on a molecular, atomic and nuclear scale. You will be introduced to the idea of equilibrium by doing Exploration 2.1.

Even if you don't do all the explorations in this unit, do read through them as they contain useful information.

Exploration 2.1   Three types of equilibrium

Apparatus:

◆ ball-bearing   ◆ watchglass

There is a tendency in the natural world for systems to attempt to minimize their potential energies, this leads to the principle of mechanical equilibrium.

(a) Place a ball-bearing in the bottom of a watchglass, then displace it to one side and let go (see Figure 2.1a). What happens?

(b) Now invert the watchglass and repeat (see Figure 2.1b). What happens this time? Try to slow the ball-bearing with your finger.

(c) Place the ball-bearing on a flat surface (see Figure 2.1c). What happens when it is displaced to one side this time?

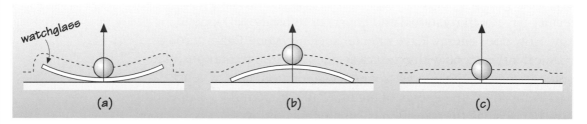

Figure 2.1   Demonstrating different types of equilibrium

Given that it ought to be possible for the ball-bearing to balance on the upturned watchglass, these phenomena show different kinds of equilibria. (When stationary, in all cases, forces on the ball-bearing add up to zero or are balanced.) But the cases are clearly different. We call them **stable**, **unstable** and **neutral equilibrium**.

 Can you think what criterion decides which kind of equilibrium we have got?

You had to do work to displace the ball in part (a), zero work in part (c) and *negative* work in part (b) (we can think of this as the ball-bearing doing work on your finger as it rolls down the glass.)

Stability is particularly important to chemical combinations of atoms and nuclear combinations of subatomic particles. If work must be done to tear a molecule apart or split a nucleus, then such a molecule or nucleus is more stable in a combined than in a fragmented state, just as a ball-bearing is more stable in the **potential well** of the watchglass. It is this idea that leads to the concepts of **binding energy** within nuclei, interatomic (chemical) bonds and intermolecular (adhesive, cohesive, surface tension) energies.

Now place the watchglass, concave side up, near the edge of the bench. Place the ball-bearing on the glass and roll it up to the edge of the glass and over the side of the bench.

Remembering that the work done by something equals its change in energy, how does the work done on the system before the 'fall' compare to the work done by the system (during the fall and collision with the ground) on the 'outside world'?

It was far less.

This is the principle behind chemical and nuclear reactions. In a chemical reaction a **catalyst** or more attractive reactant might be employed to start or sustain an **exothermic reaction** (one emitting thermal energy), in a nuclear reaction a neutron might initiate the disintegration of a nucleus. Some nuclear reactions require no initiation when the parent nuclei are unstable. Such activity is known as radioactivity.

Q2 Try to draw sketch graphs for the variation of energy and horizontal displacement for a cone stood (a) on its base, (b) on its point, (c) on its side. ◆

Knowing where to find energy is not always enough. It is often more helpful to have the energy we may need stored somehow.

 Using your list from R2, draw up a new list showing how each kind of energy may be stored – if it can.

The following list gives our answers – you may have thought of equally good alternatives – and we have expanded on them a little as a way of explanation.

Gravitational potential energy exists in any mass at some distance from the centre of the Earth, so a mass of water trapped behind a dam at altitude stores potential energy.

Kinetic energy can be stored in a moving flywheel.

Strain energy can be stored in a wound spring of a clockwork motor.

Chemical energy is stored in all molecules but, as you have just seen, these form useful sources only if less energy is used to release the stored energy than the amount of stored energy released.

Nuclear energy is stored in all the nuclei of atoms and, as for chemical energy, nuclear energy is useful only if a small amount of energy input initiates a larger output when the nucleus disintegrates or fuses.

Electromagnetic (light) energy can be stored in phosphorescent materials such as the 'glow stars' on your bedroom ceiling. (Come on, we know you've got some!)

Electrical energy can be stored in cells, batteries and capacitors.

Thermal energy is present in any material that is hot – we store it in our homes in the hot water tank. We call such thermal energy '**sensible heat**', because we know it is there by the elevated temperature we can 'sense'. But thermal energy is also present in materials that have changed from solid to liquid or from liquid to gas or vapour, even if the temperature didn't rise during the process. This is referred to as **latent heat**, suggesting that it is hidden and not associated with a temperature change. These titles are a little misleading: if you were foolish enough to put your hand in the steam issuing from a kettle spout, the painful scalding you would receive would convince you that large amounts of energy are stored in such 'hidden' situations, which can certainly be felt.

 Exploration 2.2   Sensible and latent heat, specific heat of water

Apparatus:

◆ large plastic electric kettle ◆ thermometer ◆ tongs ◆ balance

40 MINUTES

Hot water and steam can scald.

Read the power rating of the kettle from the manufacturer's label. Measure and record the temperature and mass (at least one kilogram) of water in the kettle. Close the lid, put the thermometer into the water through the spout, then switch on and time how long it takes the temperature to rise by approximately 40°C. (Use the tongs to hold the thermometer so that your hands do not come into contact with the steam.) Switch off, stir the water and record its new temperature.

Note that a temperature rise occurred: this is clearly a 'sensible' effect.

How much energy was supplied to the water? (Remember that energy supplied, Q = power × time and power = VI, so $Q = VIt$, where V is the potential difference and I the current). How much energy was supplied for each degree the water rose in temperature? How much energy was supplied for each degree rise for each kilogram of water?

This last quantity, which we are assuming is the thermal energy absorbed by a material per unit temperature rise per unit mass, is called the **specific heat capacity**, c, of the material. We use the word '**specific**' in physics to identify values given per unit quantity of stuff, almost always per unit mass.

 What units should c be in?

You divided energy by mass and temperature to find c, so in SI units the units of specific heat are $\mathrm{J\ kg^{-1}\ K^{-1}}$.

The relationship between all the terms introduced is $Q = mc\Delta\theta$, where $\Delta\theta$ denotes change in temperature: $\Delta\theta$ is positive when a rise has occurred.

The published value for the specific heat capacity of water is 4200 J kg^{-1} K^{-1}, to two significant figures. Did your result suggest the kettle element supplied too much or too little thermal energy? Make a list of possible sources of error in your experiment and estimate your overall error.

 Why might an error exist?

The body of the kettle was heated too; thermal energy was lost to the atmosphere, mainly by conduction, convection and vapour loss (evaporation). So the kettle element supplies too much thermal energy.

 How could you take these errors into account?

There are various ways to do this: one is to start with water cooled below room temperature (say 10°C cooler) and to **heat** it to 10°C above room temperature; this means that loss of thermal energy will be partially balanced by gain of thermal energy.

Now place the kettle on the balance and remove the lid (this will disable the automatic cutout, so do not let it boil dry and keep away from the steam) and switch on. Once the kettle is boiling, take readings of mass and time as the water 'boils away'. (If vibrations make measurement of mass too difficult, just take initial and final readings of m and t.)

Using your initial and final mass readings, find the mass evaporated.

Determine the energy supplied, Q, as you did in the first part.

Find the energy supplied per unit mass to evaporate the water.

 What units should this quantity be in?

You divided energy by mass, so units are J kg^{-1}.

This quantity is called the specific latent heat of vaporization, L_v, of water. The relationship between L_v, Q and m is

$$Q = L_v m$$

Now plot a graph of mass against time. There is no need to include zero mass on your vertical axis. A more accurate method to find L_v determines the rate of mass evaporation, $\Delta m/\Delta t$. This is the gradient of the graph.

Dividing $Q = L_v m$ by time t it follows that

rate of energy supply $= L_v \times$ rate of mass loss

Determine L_v again. The published value is 226 kJ kg^{-1}. What is your error?

 Can you explain any discrepancy?

No change in temperature of the kettle occurred this time, but thermal energy was lost to the surroundings again.

2.2 Fuels

Materials with nuclear and chemically stored energy are known as **fuels** if the energy given out following a reaction is greater than that required to initiate it, or greater than that taken in during the reaction. Fuels may also be considered to be means of transporting energy. While energy can't be destroyed, just changed from one form to another, fuels can clearly be used up – their products become dispersed and can't be used again. Unless harnessed usefully, the energy given out during burning is dispersed too, irrecoverably; but it is not destroyed. So we may destroy a fuel, by burning a bag of coal, for example, but not the energy in it. If energy may be stored and can't be created or destroyed, just transferred, then we know that the total amount of energy in an **isolated system** must remain constant. In this respect, there is a rough analogy with money: in a market at any instant, there is a certain amount of money – in people's pockets, stallholders' tills, on the ground, etc. People may give money to a stallholder or vice versa, but the total amount of money in the system remains the same.

 If we know the stallholders made £10 000 one day, then how much have the customers spent? What can you say about the amount of money each has at the end of the day?

The customers have spent £10 000. However, the difference between what they have in their pockets at the end of the day and at the beginning may be more or less than this. The same is true for the stallholders. Either may have lost some or been robbed, or they could have got some from a cash dispenser. Perhaps the market manager collects stall rental and carries it away (analogous to energy losses from a mechanical system). You can see that it is important to define the boundaries of the system.

Calculations could be done to find out each element of the day's financial transactions by simple arithmetic. Just as pounds may be used to measure several different kinds of financial commodity, be it tax, wages, debt, takings, expenditure, profit, so too the joule measures different kinds of energy, work done and heat. Energy, then, is part of an accounting system in physics, but we use the joule as the unit, not the pound sterling.

 Can you think of any other analogies between energy and money?

Different countries use different currencies and there are different energy units too.

2.3 The biosphere

In our context of looking at aspects of energy in the environment, we need to study movements of energy. Important transfers take place in the thin shell around Earth that supports life. This shell includes the land surface and oceans, the atmosphere to at least 10 000 m, and the crust to a depth of several hundred metres below the land surface and the sea bed. This shell is called the **biosphere** (see Figure 2.2).

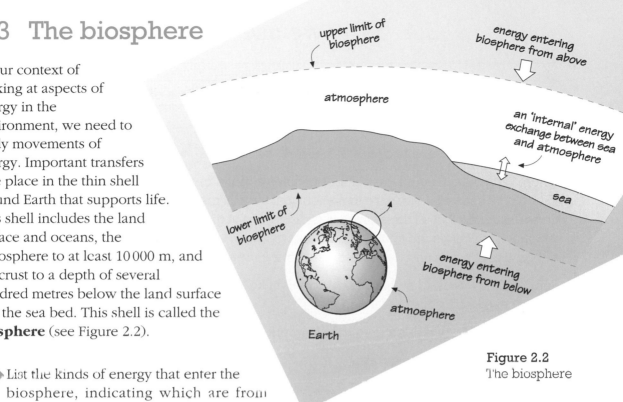

Figure 2.2
The biosphere

> List the kinds of energy that enter the biosphere, indicating which are from 'above' and which are from 'below'. Ignore 'internal' forms of energy such as winds.

From above, electromagnetic radiation from the Sun and other stars, from below, radioactive decay and thermal energy cause an upward flow of geothermal energy.

We can add to these. Cosmic rays come from above but are fairly insignificant in terms of the total energy arriving. Chemical energy in fuels is mined from deep in Earth's crust and so forms an energy flow or flux from below. You may be surprised to learn that the energy transferred to the tides on Earth results in the decay of Earth's rotation, the Moon's orbit about Earth and Earth's orbit round the Sun.

Outputs from the biosphere are largely reflected and re-emitted solar electromagnetic energy and longwave radiated thermal energy. Many energy transfers within the biosphere ultimately end in thermal energy, except a small amount stored as chemical energy (for example, in fossil fuels; although, following human exploitation, this will no doubt eventually end up as thermal energy too).

By far the largest input is solar radiation. Without a continuous supply of energy from the Sun, plants would stop growing, an environment suitable for life would not exist and life would cease. Luckily for us, the Sun is expected to continue to shine for several thousand million years. Unfortunately, the lifestyle of developed (and rapidly developing) nations is based on a very intensive use of energy, demanding the consumption of large amounts of fossil fuels to supplement the Sun's diffuse supply of energy.

2.4 Why we use energy

20 MINUTES

E Exploration 2.3 Human power and the value of labour

Apparatus:

♦ 2 kg and 5 kg weights or dumb-bells ♦ metre rules ♦ stopwatch

Using a stopwatch, count the number of times a friend can lift the weights in about 30 seconds. Measure the height that they lift the weights each time. Assuming that all the energy was dissipated at the end of each repetition, calculate the total potential energy given to the weights during this process and the power developed. (See Figure 2.3a.)

Suppose they worked at this all day (for eight hours), how much work would have been done?

How many kW h of work did your friend perform?

Your friend also raises their arm, but the work involved in doing so was hardly useful.

Electricity costs about 7p per kW h; so what was the work expended in lifting the weight worth?

If your friend had demanded pay, at a rate of say £3 per hour, what would it have cost to employ them?

Perhaps you can see why, from this example, for mechanical work, it is economically better to use power tools and electrical appliances than to have people working by hand. Furthermore, as you found out, repetitive, mechanical work is often quite boring. Of course, using power tools means the worker loses out in terms of fitness!

Design and undertake a similar investigation to estimate power output of your friend running up stairs (see Figure 2.3b). (Or maybe it is your turn to work!)

 Why do you obtain different values of power output?

We considered only useful work in the first case; you could say the climber did no *useful* work at all (power = zero) since they didn't lift anything but themselves.

Suppose an average household uses 4500 kW h in one year for non-heating purposes. In ancient and medieval times, in wealthy households this work would have been supplied mainly by slaves or servants. If a person can do about 2.5 MJ of work in one day, estimate how many slaves or servants this household would need. Can you draw any conclusions about the social structure of older societies from this?

> Don't drop the weights on your feet, don't lift too much, be careful on the stairs. Students who do not participate in normal PE for medical reasons should not lift weights or run up stairs.

From your investigation, you should now appreciate that using machines can save considerable amounts of human labour and allow us to do more with our time. We can then earn more and purchase more, possibly raising our quality of life. Of course, much of this 'quality of life' means more energy consumption. Some may be legitimate – better healthcare, improved living conditions. Some is more frivolous – more gadgets or unnecessary travel. Whatever our value judgement on this issue, it is a fact that energy consumption has risen considerably since the Industrial Revolution because of an increase in both quality of life and population. Figure 2.4 shows the changes in UK population over the last 600 years.

Figure 2.3
(a) Lifting weights,
(b) running up stairs

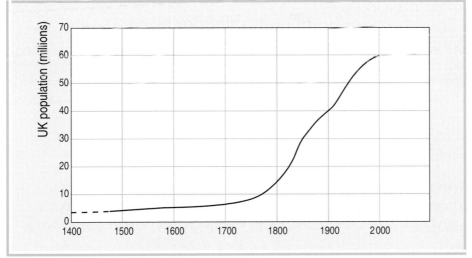

Figure 2.4
UK population between the years 1400 and 2000

It was once thought that, at best, the world population might level out at double its current value of about 5.8×10^9. In fact, some recent estimates are more optimistic (if you can call it that!), projecting a levelling off at 10.6×10^9 in 2100, and falling back to 10.35×10^9 about 50 years later.

We can use the following mathematical rule of thumb to help us analyse growth (and decay).

The time taken for a quantity to double (or half) is found by dividing 69 by the percentage growth (or decay) rate.

For example, suppose you invest some money with interest paid at 3% per year. Divide 69 by this number and you get 23. So it will take 23 years for your money to double. (70 may be used for rough work.) Why this magic number 69?

If you have read the SLIPP unit *Physics in Space*, you may recall from work on radioactivity in Appendix 2.1 (pp. 43–4) of that unit that half-life, $t_{1/2}$, is related to decay constant, λ, by

$$t_{1/2} = \frac{\ln 2}{\lambda}$$

Similarly for a growth situation, doubling life, t_2, is given by

$$t_2 = \frac{\ln 2}{\lambda}$$

Here, λ is a growth factor, not a decay constant. If you look up $\ln 2$ you will find it is approximately 0.69. If you want to use percentage values for λ you need to multiply this number by 100, hence 69.

 At a growth rate of 1.7% per year, what is the doubling time for the world population?

$$\frac{69}{1.7 \text{ per year}} = 41 \text{ years (to two significant figures)}$$

 What is the initial increase per year in terms of numbers of people?

$$\frac{1.7}{100} \text{ per year} \times 5.8 \times 10^9 \text{ people} \approx 100 \text{ million people per year}$$

Gross national product (GNP) measures the wealth creation of a country per annum. When GNP is divided by population, the result is called per capita GNP and this is a rough indicator of standard of living.

 Look at Figure 2.5. In rough terms, what can you conclude about the relationship between standard of living and energy consumption?

They are roughly proportional.

Remember, this is only a rough result. To emphasize this, answer the following questions.

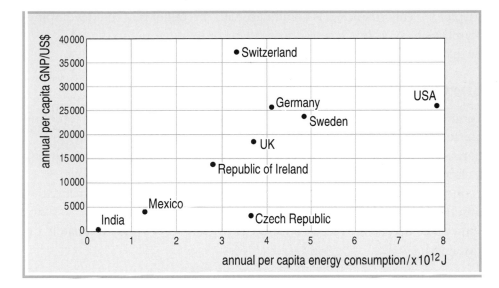

Figure 2.5
Per capita energy consumption compared with per capita wealth creation

 What can you say about the UK and the Czech Republic?

Although each member of the population of the UK and of the Czech Republic consumes the same amount of energy on average (per year), each member of the UK creates nearly six times more wealth than each member of the Czech Republic.

 What can you say about the USA and Germany?

Although each member of the population of both countries creates the same amount of wealth per year, Germans consume half as much energy on average (per year) as citizens of the United States.

The correlation between per capita energy consumption and per capita GNP is not now as hard and fast as it was; over the past two decades, many countries have raised their GNP whilst hardly raising energy consumption at all. As far as developing countries are concerned, fuel in the form of wood and human and animal power are often neglected in statistics; some estimate that fuel in the form of wood contributes 10% or more to total world energy use.

 If you were prime minister, given our discussion so far, what could you do to cut your country's energy consumption?

You might suggest trying to reduce population growth or reducing living standards, or both

Population control policies have been undertaken in some countries, notably China and India, where they have been partially successful. In many developing countries these efforts, particularly when encouraged by external institutions, are seen as undesirable and viewed with suspicion. This suspicion is combined with the belief that the developing countries have a right to enjoy a standard of living equal to that of developed countries. What is your view? Discuss this with a friend.

Energy reserves

To understand the constraints on energy consumption, we need to define our terms carefully. As far as fossil fuels are concerned, **reserves** are deposits known to exist that can be extracted economically using current technology; **resources** are deposits likely to exist that *might* prove economical to extract in the future. Cautious financial rules regarding the description of reserves often cause them to be underestimated; sometimes up to nine times so-called 'proved reserves' may ultimately be extracted.

Q3 Using the data in Table 2.2, calculate to the nearest year how long each fuel will last at present rates of consumption for the UK. ◆

Table 2.2 Fossil fuel reserves and consumption rates, UK, world and USA, by type, including calorific values, and population (1995)

Fuel	Density/ kg m^{-3} (approx.)	Calorific value	UK (population 58 million)		World (population 5292 million)		USA (population 260 million)	
			Annual consumption*	Reserves	Annual consumption	Reserves	Annual consumption	Reserves
Coal	2300	30.6 MJ kg^{-1}	71.7 Mt	2500 Mt	3316 Mt	1 031 610 Mt	741.6 Mt	240 558 Mt
Oil	680	43.2 MJ kg^{-1}	81.7 Mt	600 Mt	3226.9 Mt	138 300 Mt	806.8 Mt	3700 Mt
Gas	0.60	38.0 MJ m^{-3}	7.31×10^{10} m^3	7.00×10^{12} m^3	2.093×10^{12} m^3	1.397×10^{14} m^3	6.216×10^{11} m^3	4.6×10^{12} m^3
Hydro-electricity	–	–	6.0×10^9 kW h	–	2.622×10^{12} kW h	–	3.1×10^{11} kW h	–
Nuclear	–	–	2.76×10^{11} kW h	–	7.16×10^{12} kW h	–	2.2×10^{12} kW h	–
Wood	600	8–16 MJ kg^{-1}	–	–	–	–	—	—

* Neglects approximately 18×10^9 kW h of electricity and heat from renewable sources.

Q4 What is wrong with this prediction? ◆

Further criticisms may be levelled at the crudity of this calculation. The cost of a fuel will certainly rise with its scarcity, so it is likely that none of the three fossil fuels will be exhausted before the others; if oil began to run out, coal would doubtless be converted into some kind of liquid substitute. Fresh stocks may be found and extraction of previously uneconomic stocks will become worthwhile.

Apparatus:

- ◆ fuel calorimeter ◆ power supply ◆ ammeter ◆ voltmeter
- ◆ leads ◆ spirit lamp ◆ filter pump ◆ balance

Fuel calorimeters can be hazardous. Wear eye protection and use a safety screen.

Some of these effects and trends may be accounted for if we employ the concept of **calorific value**. A calorific value is simply the amount of energy in one kilogram (or one cubic metre for gases) of fuel in some common unit. Using a fuel calorimeter as shown in Figure 2.6 we can deduce approximately the energy output of a fuel. We can do this by burning a known mass of the fuel in a spirit lamp placed inside the fuel calorimeter and noting the rise in temperature of the water after the combustion products are exhausted; we can then estimate the number of joules per kilogram in the fuel. This is most easily done by repeating the experiment, using an electrical heater, the output of which can easily be quantified, and raising the apparatus's temperature by the same amount in the same time.

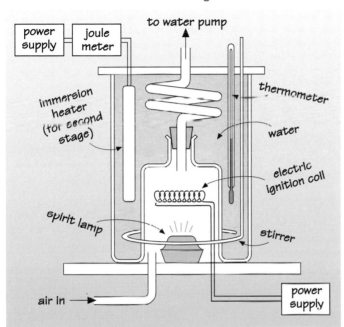

Figure 2.6 A fuel calorimeter

Remember to note the initial and final temperatures and the time, t_1, in seconds during which the fuel burns.

Remember also that energy supplied electrically, $W = VIt_2$, where V is the potential difference across the heating filament and I the current flowing during time t_2. If you have used a joule meter, you will obtain a direct value of W.

This energy supplied electrically is assumed to be equal to the energy supplied by the spirit lamp. This is true only if the initial and final temperatures are the same, and if the heating period is the same, i.e. $t_1 = t_2$. There should be no major problem obtaining the same temperatures, but your teacher can offer advice and refinements to the procedure. You may have to repeat the electrical part, adjusting V until this is the case, or accept that there will be some inaccuracy.

So, $VIt_2 = mk$, or $W = mk$, where k is the calorific value and m is the mass of fuel in the spirit lamp.

Calculate and record k, including its units.

Exploration 2.5 Making wood gas

10 MINUTES

Perform this exploration in a fume cupboard.

Apparatus:

◆ Bunsen burner ◆ two boiling tubes
◆ bungs and glass tubes (one drawn to a nozzle)
◆ wood chips ◆ matches and spills

Set up the apparatus as shown in Figure 2.7 and heat the boiling tube with a Bunsen burner.

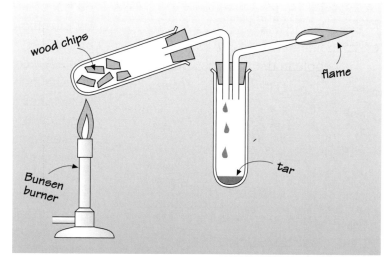

Figure 2.7 Making wood gas

Try lighting the jet coming out of the nozzle with a spill periodically until no more gas appears.

What do you think is left in each boiling tube?

Coal was converted into charcoal, gas and tar in a similar way for many years. We can conclude, then, that an inconvenient fuel may be converted to another more convenient form, but it requires equipment and energy to do so. Furthermore, you may be left with products that are of little use or are pollutants. There may also be storage problems – when domestic gas was produced from coal, all major towns had large gas stores called gasometers.

Data analysis exercise – energy reserves

Using the information in Table 2.2, answer the following questions, preferably using spreadsheet techniques where appropriate. If you do not have access to spreadsheet software, share the arithmetic between friends. Answers are given at the end of the section.

(a) Work out the energy per unit volume in coal, oil and gas, using the data given.

(b) At current rates of consumption, work out how long each of the different fuel reserves should last for the USA and for the world.

(c) Using the calorific values given, convert the reserves and consumption of all the fuels into joules and work out how long each country's reserves of fossil fuels will last, given that fuels will no doubt be converted into other kinds as each begins to run out. Assume 100% conversion efficiencies and, for now, neglect the contributions of hydroelectricity and nuclear electricity.

(d) Work out per capita (per person) consumption for the world, the UK and the USA for fossil fuel.

(e) Suppose everyone in the world consumed energy at the same average rate as people in the USA; how long would fossil fuels last at the current population levels?

(f) By what factor would hydroelectricity and nuclear electricity have to expand to cope with these demands?

(g) What assumptions have you made during these calculations and are they reasonable?

(h) What do you conclude from your work? ◆

You will need your answers to this exercise for later work.

 Exploration 2.6   Efficiency of cooking

Apparatus:

◆ beaker ◆ solid model steam engine fuel (about 2 cm^3) ◆ thermometer ◆ balance

The **energy efficiency** of any process is given by

$$\text{efficiency} = \frac{\text{useful energy output}}{\text{total energy input}}$$

This gives values between 0 and 1. (If percentages are required, the equation needs to be multiplied by 100.)

In this investigation, you are going to heat some water in a beaker over about 2 cm^3 model steam engine solid fuel. Decide what measurements you should take to evaluate the efficiency of the process.

Check your ideas with your teacher then carry out your experiment.

Only one group of students should do this exploration at a time and the lab should be well ventilated, as vapours from the fuel may be toxic. Wash your hands after handling the fuel.

Growth of consumption is one of the most important factors to take into account when considering lifetimes of resources.

 (a) Suppose that you have 63 Smarties and you eat them at the rate of one per minute. How long would it take you to eat them all? (b) If you change your rate of consumption every minute so that it is double the rate that it was the minute before, how long would it take you to eat them all now?

(a) 63 minutes. (b) 6 minutes. (You can test this experimentally if you like!)

Q5 Look at Figure 2.8. Use the values you obtained in parts (b) and (e) of the data analysis exercise to estimate the lifetime of current world reserves if there was a 2% per annum growth rate. ◆

Figure 2.8
Lifetime, t, of finite energy resources for various percentage growth rates, r, in consumption ($t = 100$ years when $r = 0$)

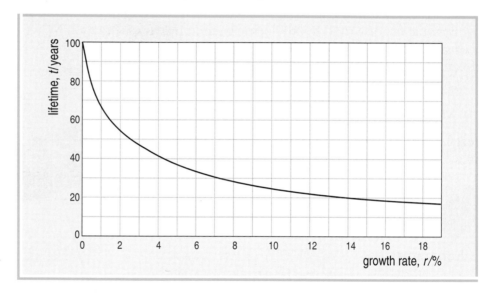

2.5 Pollution

So far we have not considered a major aspect of the use of fuels. While scarcity of fuel is reason enough to be anxious about future supply, consumption of fossil fuels that release carbon and sulphur into the atmosphere causes further problems. When fossil fuels and **biofuels** are burnt, carbon in them reacts with oxygen in the air to form carbon dioxide.

 Which sources of energy do not produce carbon dioxide?

Nuclear, wind, geothermal and hydroelectric power. However, nuclear power produces radioactive pollution, and both nuclear and geothermal power produce thermal pollution. Hydroelectric power can also be a cause of pollution – plant and animal life submerged in the regions flooded to produce reservoirs behind dams can decay and produce methane.

Pollution is narrowly defined as the modification of the environment by the release of noxious matter, rendering it harmful or unpleasant to life. Too much pollution can overload ecosystems – elements of the biosphere – whether on the scale of a pond, a local park, a wood, a forest, a river, an ocean or even the entire biosphere itself. Pollution can take many forms: it can be a substance (solid particles, liquid or a gas or vapour) or it can be in the form of radioactive decay products or heat. All these can pervade the atmosphere, water, ground and the plants and animals that inhabit these. If interpreted more broadly, pollution can also take the form of undesirable vibrations like noise or tremors from machinery, or light that obscures the stars in the night sky. Some effects are secondary, like algal blooms or heat haze – one pollutant causes another pollutant to thrive or manifest itself. Pollution can simply be a nuisance or it can affect our health (including our psychological well-being), habitat and food production.

Light pollution over the UK – the lightest areas have the most light pollution

 List some examples of pollution prevalent in the industrial world for each kind mentioned above.

You may have included CO_2; H_2O; SO_2; **NO_x**; CH_4; CO; O_3; ash and **particulates**, hot water effluent from power stations, vehicle and road noise and vibration. (*Note:* Not all of these pollutants are a result of power production – e.g. much CH_4 is produced by agriculture and CO_2 is given off during cement production.

2.6 Solutions to an energy crisis

It is clear then that the so-called energy crisis is potentially a real one and we have already hinted at two solutions:

■ cut the population and so cut energy demand

■ cut living standards and so lower energy consumption.

Can you think of any more?

We could

■ make what we use go further (conserve energy)

■ exploit alternative forms of energy.

Population control is not really appropriate in the UK since here, as in much of the developed world, the death rate just balances the birth rate. We could exploit alternative supplies, which might include nuclear, solar, wind and water power. We could practise conservation by simply lowering the standard of living – by living in colder homes and wearing more clothes in winter, for example. But this is unlikely to be attractive to politicians or the public. An acceptable conservation policy must provide ways of not only using less fuel but using fuel more efficiently. Unfortunately, conservation often results in using the same amount of energy as before; for example, with better insulation we simply have warmer homes and use the same amount of fuel. Conservation measures might include the employment of even higher insulation standards and the re-use of waste heat from thermal power stations for district heating. In Section 3, we assess the potential of these options, starting by looking at the present demand for energy.

Q6   If you were prime minister how could you promote each of the four options at the beginning of Section 2.6. ◆

Achievements

After working through this section you should be able to:

- recall that all interactions involve transfer of energy
- recall that there are just two kinds of energy: potential and kinetic
- use energy concepts as a kind of accounting system
- recall that fuels are abundant yet finite
- define fuels, resources and reserves
- appreciate that fuels and work have value in financial terms
- determine calorific value and energy density of fuels
- consider, more critically, economic information and projections
- suggest some solutions to the problem of energy shortage
- understand that burning fossil fuels leads to the release of carbon dioxide into the atmosphere
- appreciate that while nuclear and hydroelectric power do not release carbon dioxide they do have other problems associated with them.

Glossary

Binding energy   Unit: joule (J). The energy that binds neutrons and protons in a nucleus. Binding energy results from their loss of mass when combined compared with their isolated masses, $E = mc^2$.

Biofuel   A fuel from a biological origin, e.g. methane from sewage or decaying plant matter; wood fuel harvested from natural forests or cultivated in coppices; alcohols distilled from sugarcane. (Biomass is a general term sometimes used for the biological matter representing a natural chemical feedstock from which biofuels can be made.)

Biosphere   The region of Earth's crust and atmosphere inhabited by living matter.

Calorific value   The energy available from a fuel when it is completely burnt, expressed as units of energy per unit of weight or volume of the fuel. The gross or higher calorific value is the total energy available; the net or lower calorific value is the total energy less the latent heat of the water vapour from the combustion of hydrogen plus any water in the original fuel. The power industry tends to use net calorific value, the boiler industry gross calorific value.

Catalyst   A substance that accelerates (or retards) a chemical reaction but undergoes no permanent chemical change itself.

Chemical energy   Energy associated with the bonds between atoms making up molecules.

Efficiency   Ratio of useful output energy (or work or power) to total input energy (or work or power) for a system. Efficiency has no units but is often expressed as a percentage.

Electromagnetic energy   Unit: joule (J). Energy associated with electric and magnetic oscillating fields; it is usually in the form of travelling waves. It ranges from waves of kilometre lengths, e.g. radio waves, through centimetre radar waves to microwaves, infrared, visual, ultraviolet, X-rays and gamma-rays. These last have wavelengths of about 10^{-14} m. In general, the shorter the wavelength the more damaging these waves are and the larger the energy packet (quantum) in which they arrive. For animal and plants, microwaves are an anomaly to this rule, since microwaves may oscillate at the frequency most suited to setting up resonant oscillations in the water molecules found in living tissue. These vibrations ultimately produce molecular vibrational energy, i.e. thermal energy. The names of the different electromagnetic radiations arise solely from the various means of production, detection and relative wavelength of such waves. Electromagnetic quanta arrive in packets of energy, called photons: $E = hf$, where h is Planck's constant.

Equilibrium   The condition of a body when there is no resultant force on it in any direction and no resultant moment of a force about any point. See also *Neutral equilibrium*, *Stable equilibrium* and *Unstable equilibrium*.

Exothermic reaction   A process in which thermal energy is emitted.

Fuel   Material that stores energy in chemical or nuclear form and gives a net energy output from a reaction.

Gravitational potential energy   Unit: joule (J). The energy of a body or particle due to its position in a gravitational field.

Gross national product   A measure of the wealth creation of a country per annum (year). When divided by population, per capita gross national product becomes a rough indicator of standard of living.

Heat   (Verb) To transfer thermal energy.

Internal energy   Unit: joule (J); symbol: U. The sum of the potential and kinetic energies of all molecules or atoms in a sample.

Isolated system   When applying the law of conservation of energy to energy flows within a system or device, inputs and outputs from the system must be known. If they are zero, however, the system may be taken to be isolated.

Kinetic energy   Unit: joule (J). The energy of a body or particle due to its motion.

Latent heat   Unit: joule (J). The thermal energy absorbed or released when a substance changes phase at constant temperature.

Neutral equilibrium   A state of equilibrium where the potential energy is unchanged by a small displacement, i.e. the object remains in the new position.

NO$_x$ A general term for those oxides of nitrogen that are produced by fuel combustion and eventually discharged to the atmosphere, and considered deleterious emissions.

Particulates   Particles of solid matter, usually of very small size, derived from a fuel, either directly or as a result of incomplete combustion, and considered deleterious emissions.

Potential energy   Unit: joule (J). The energy of a body or particle due to its position. See also *Gravitational potential energy*.

Potential well   A location in which energy must be given to a particle for it to escape, i.e. where its potential energy is lower than if it were outside the region. An orbiting satellite or charge is in such a well.

Reserves   Deposits known to exist that can be extracted economically using current technology.

Resources   Deposits likely to exist that *might* prove economical to extract in the future.

Sensible heat   A change in thermal energy of a body associated with a change of temperature. The use of 'sensible', meaning 'able to be sensed' is misleading: latent heat effects may also be sensed, sometimes more acutely than sensible ones.

Specific   An adjective usually meaning 'per unit mass'.

Specific heat capacity   Unit: joule per kilogram per kelvin ($J\,kg^{-1}\,K^{-1}$). The energy required to raise the temperature of unit mass of a material by unit temperature.

Stable equilibrium   A state of equilibrium where the potential energy of the system is at a minimum and will increase with any small displacement, i.e. the object will return to its original position.

Strain (or elastic) energy   Unit: joule (J). The energy stored in a body following strain.

Thermal energy   Unit: joule (J); symbol: Q. The energy supplied to or lost from a body as a result of heat transfer.

Unstable equilibrium   A state of equilibrium where the potential energy of the system is at a maximum and will decrease with any small displacement, i.e. the object will move to a more stable position.

Work   Unit: joule (J). Mechanical energy in transit. A measure of energy transferred by the action of a force applied over a distance. Movement is always involved, even if it is only a change of shape. It can be expressed in terms of newton metres (N m) as well as joules (J).

Answers to Ready to Study test

R1

See the Glossary for definitions of the terms.

R2

In addition to those given in R1, you may have listed: nuclear, sound, electromagnetic, electrical (static and current), magnetic, and strain energy.

R3

(a) Yes. The engine thrust must be larger than the weight of the rocket in order to accelerate. The exhaust gases do work on the rocket.

(b) No. There is no resultant force on the rocket in this situation.

(c) Yes. The tow does work on the skier.

(d) Yes. The skier does work on the piste and atmosphere as their gravitational potential energy is lost.

(e) No. There is no resultant force on the book and no displacement.

R4

(a)
Weight of cement lifted

$$= mass \times gravitational\ field\ strength$$
$$= mg$$
$$= 2.00 \times 1000\,kg \times 9.81\,N\,kg^{-1}$$
$$= 1.96 \times 10^{4}\ N$$

   (to three significant figures)

(b)
Potential energy gained $= mgh$

$$= 1.96 \times 10^{4}\ N \times 15\,m$$
$$= 2.94 \times 10^{5}\ J$$

(c)

Work done by pump = gravitational potential energy gained by cement

$$= 2.94 \times 10^5 \text{ J}$$

(if kinetic energy, E_k, gained is negligible).

(d)

$$\text{Output power of pump} = \frac{\text{work done}}{\text{time taken}}$$

$$= \frac{2.94 \times 10^5 \text{ J}}{50\text{s}}$$

$$= 5.88 \times 10^3 \text{ W}$$

$$= 5.88 \text{ kW}$$

(e)

$$\text{Efficiency of pump} = \frac{\text{useful work output}}{\text{total energy input}}$$

$$= \frac{5.88 \text{ kW}}{10 \text{kW}}$$

$$= 0.588 \text{ or } 58.8\%$$

(f)

Power consumption of pump = 10.0 kW.

Energy 'consumed' in one hour = 10.0 kW h (by definition of the unit).

Energy 'consumed' in eight hours
$$= 80.0 \text{ kW h}.$$

R5

Energy cannot be created or destroyed, it can only be transferred from one form to another.

R6

See Figure 2.9 and Table 2.3.

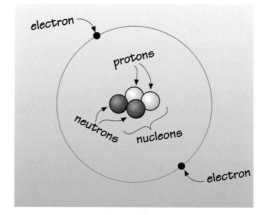

Figure 2.9 Bohr model of the atom for helium

Table 2.3

	Electron	Proton	Neutron
charge/e	−1	+1	0
comparative mass	1	1836	1839
mass/kg	9.109×10^{-31}	1.673×10^{-27}	1.675×10^{-27}

R7

Volume of 4.0 litres of petrol $= \dfrac{4.0}{1000} \text{m}^3$

$$= 4.0 \times 10^{-3} \text{m}^3$$

Mass = density × volume

therefore

mass of 4.0 litres of petrol

$$= 0.68 \times 10^3 \text{kg m}^{-3} \times 4.0 \times 10^{-3} \text{m}^3$$

$$= 2.72 \text{kg}$$

$$= 2.7 \text{kg (to two significant figures)}$$

R8

Kinetic energy is given by

$$E_k = \frac{1}{2} m v^2$$

so kinetic energy of the bullet is

$$E_{k \text{ bullet}} = \frac{1}{2} 20 \times 10^{-3} \text{kg} \times \left(300 \text{ms}^{-1}\right)^2$$

$$= 9.0 \times 10^2 \text{ J}$$

Velocity of the lorry is

$$v_{\text{lorry}} = \frac{80 \times 1000 \text{m}}{60 \times 60 \text{s}}$$

$$= 22.2 \text{ms}^{-1}$$

and kinetic energy of the lorry is

$$E_{k \text{ lorry}} = \frac{1}{2} 44 \times 10^3 \text{kg} \times \left(22.2 \text{ms}^{-1}\right)^2$$

$$= 10\,842.48 \text{kJ}$$

$$= 1.1 \times 10^7 \text{ J (to two significant figures)}$$

The kinetic energy of the lorry is approximately 12 000 times bigger than that of the bullet whereas its mass is approximately 2 million times greater.

R9

Wavelength of photon, $\lambda = 550 \times 10^{-9}$ m. Using the wave equation $c = f\lambda$ gives

$$f = \frac{c}{\lambda}$$

$$= \frac{3.0 \times 10^8 \text{ ms}^{-1}}{550 \times 10^{-9} \text{ m}}$$

$$= 5.45 \times 10^{14} \text{ s}^{-1}$$

$$= 5.5 \times 10^{14} \text{ Hz (to two significant figures)}$$

Photon energy is given by

$$E = hf$$

$$= 6.6 \times 10^{-34} \text{ Js} \times 5.45 \times 10^{14} \text{ s}^{-1}$$

$$= 3.6 \times 10^{-19} \text{ J (to two significant figures)}$$

R10

The potential energy lost by the apple is given by

$$E_{\text{pot}} = mgh$$

$$= 0.20 \text{kg} \times 10 \text{N kg}^{-1} \times 5.0 \text{m}$$

$$= 10 \text{ J}$$

R11

Remember that units may be treated algebraically.

$$1 \text{W} = 1 \text{Js}^{-1}$$

$$1 \text{kW} = 1000 \text{Js}^{-1}$$

$$1 \text{h} = 3600 \text{s}$$

therefore

$$1 \text{kW h} = 1000 \text{Js}^{-1} \times 3600 \text{s}$$

$$= 3.6 \times 10^6 \text{ J}$$

See Table 2.4.

Table 2.4

Prefix	Standard form	Symbol
tera	$\times 10^{12}$	T
giga	$\times 10^{9}$	G
mega	$\times 10^{6}$	M
kilo	$\times 10^{3}$	k
hecto	$\times 10^{2}$	h
deci	$\times 10^{-1}$	d
centi	$\times 10^{-2}$	c
milli	$\times 10^{-3}$	m
micro	$\times 10^{-6}$	μ
nano	$\times 10^{-9}$	n
pico	$\times 10^{-12}$	p

Answers to questions in the text

Q1

The speed of the car is $v = 50$ km h^{-1}.

Converting this to SI units gives

$$v = \frac{50 \times 1000\,\text{m}}{60 \times 60\,\text{s}}$$

$$= 13.9\,\text{ms}^{-1}$$

Kinetic energy gained by the car is

$$E_k = \frac{1}{2}mv^2$$

$$= \frac{1}{2}1500\,\text{kg} \times \left(13.9\,\text{ms}^{-1}\right)^2$$

$$= 145\,\text{kJ}$$

$$= 1.45 \times 10^5\,\text{J}$$

Strain energy in the spring is

$$E_{\text{strain}} = \frac{1}{2}kx^2$$

$$= \frac{2.0 \times 10^5\,\text{N m}^{-1} \times x^2}{2}$$

$$= x^2 \times 10^5\,\text{N m}^{-1}$$

Assuming energy losses are negligible

$$x^2 \times 10^5\,\text{N m}^{-1} = 1.45 \times 10^5\,\text{J}$$

$$x^2 = 1.45\,\text{m}^2$$

$$x = 1.2\,\text{m}$$

(to two significant figures)

Q2

See Figure 2.10.

Q3

Dividing reserves by annual consumption yields:
35 years' worth of coal left
7 years' worth of oil left
10 years' worth of gas left.

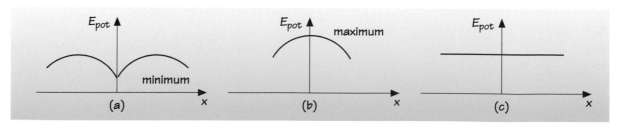

Figure 2.10 Answer to Question 2

Q4

The data used are reserves not resources, therefore, in time, more resources could be classed as reserves, and with developing technology or increasing prices it could become economical to extract them. Also, the present rate of use is likely to change.

Q5

From Figure 2.8, you can see that with 2% growth, a 100 year lifetime reduces to about 55 years, so our 134 year range for the world in part (b) becomes $134 \times \dfrac{55}{100} = 74$ years and our 26 year range in part (e) becomes $26 \times \dfrac{55}{100} = 14$ years. This assumes a continuously growing consumption, whereas it is more likely, as resources get scarce, that consumption will fall again. Nevertheless, ultimately, finite resources will expire.

Q6

You could use fiscal measures such as taxation, incentives such as education, or legal measures such as regulation.

Solution to data analysis exercise on p. 28

(a) To find the energy per unit volume, we need to relate the energy in the fuel, *usually* given per unit mass as calorific value, to volume, using the definition of calorific value and density.

$$k = \frac{\text{energy output of fuel}}{\text{mass}} = \frac{E}{m}$$

and

$$\rho = \frac{\text{mass}}{\text{volume}} = \frac{m}{V}$$

Rearranging and combining these two equations gives

$$\frac{E}{V} = \frac{km}{m/p}$$
$$= kp$$

So, for coal

$$\frac{E}{V} = 30.6 \times 10^6 \ \text{J kg}^{-1} \times 2300 \ \text{kg m}^{-3}$$
$$= 7.04 \times 10^{10} \ \text{J m}^{-3}$$

and for oil

$$\frac{E}{V} = 43.2 \times 10^6 \ \text{J kg}^{-1} \times 680 \ \text{kg m}^{-3}$$
$$= 2.94 \times 10^{10} \ \text{J m}^{-3}$$

$\dfrac{E}{V}$ is already given for gas in Table 2.2 as $38 \ \text{MJ m}^{-3}$, or $3.8 \times 10^8 \ \text{J m}^{-3}$.

(b) The figures in Table 2.5 are generated by dividing each fossil reserve by the annual consumption of that fossil fuel. You have already worked out the UK range for Question 3, but we have included them here for consistency.

(c) The result of converting all the above data into joules is shown in Table 2.6 overleaf. (For individual fuel lifetimes (ranges) this step is unnecessary; however, working in consistent units from the start is always a good idea, and we need to convert to joules later anyway.)

Table 2.5

	UK range in years	World range in years	USA range in years
coal	34.87	311.10	324.38
oil	7.34	42.86	4.59
gas	9.58	66.75	7.40

Table 2.6

	UK annual consumption/J	reserves/J	World annual consumption/J	reserves/J	USA annual consumption/J	reserves/J
coal	2.194×10^{18}	7.65×10^{19}	1.01496×10^{20}	3.1567266×10^{22}	2.269296×10^{19}	7.3610748×10^{21}
oil	3.52944×10^{18}	2.592×10^{19}	1.3940208×10^{20}	5.97456×10^{21}	3.485376×10^{19}	1.5984×10^{20}
gas	2.7778×10^{18}	2.66×10^{19}	7.9534×10^{19}	5.3086×10^{21}	2.3628×10^{19}	1.748×10^{20}
hydro-electricity	2.16×10^{16}		9.4392×10^{18}		1.116×10^{18}	
nuclear electricity	9.936×10^{17}		2.5776×10^{19}		7.92×10^{18}	

These are then all expressed in terms of 10^{15} J (see Table 2.7). This reveals their relative size clearly and saves number crunching.

Table 2.7

	UK annual consumption/ 10^{15} J	reserves/ 10^{15} J	World annual consumption/ 10^{15} J	reserves/ 10^{15} J	USA annual consumption/ 10^{15} J	reserves/ 10^{15} J
coal	2194.02	76 500.00	101 469.60	31 567 266.00	22 692.96	7 361 074.80
oil	3529.44	25 920.00	139 402.08	5 974 560.00	34 853.76	159 840.00
gas	2777.80	26 600.00	79 534.00	5 308 600.00	23 620.80	174 800.00
hydro-electricity	21.60		9439.20		11 16.00	
nuclear electricity	993.60		25 776.00		7920.00	

Total fossil reserves and consumption in 10^{15} J are given in Table 2.8.

Table 2.8

	UK annual consumption/ 10^{15} J	reserves/ 10^{15} J	World annual consumption/ 10^{15} J	reserves/ 10^{15} J	USA annual consumption/ 10^{15} J	reserves/ 10^{15} J
	8501.26	129 020.00	320 405.68	42 850 426.00	81 167.52	7 695 714.80

Hydro- and nuclear electricity consumption in 10^{15} J are given in Table 2.9.

Table 2.9

UK annual consumption/ 10^{15} J	World annual consumption/ 10^{15} J	USA annual consumption/ 10^{15} J
1015.20	35 215.20	9036.00

Total energy consumptions in 10^{15} J are given in Table 2.10.

Table 2.10

UK annual consumption/ 10^{15} J	World annual consumption/ 10^{15} J	USA annual consumption/ 10^{15} J
951 646	355 620.88	90 203.52

The ranges for all fossil fuels combined in Table 2.11 are generated by dividing total fossil reserves by total annual consumption – these will be useful to you later in Question 5.

Table 2.11

UK	World	USA
15.18 years	133.74 years	94.81 years

(d) Annual per capita fossil fuel consumption in joules is shown in Table 2.12.

Table 2.12

UK annual per capita consumption/ 10^{15} J	World annual per capita consumption/ 10^{15} J	USA annual per capita consumption/ 10^{15} J
$1.465\,73 \times 10^{11}$	$6.054\,52 \times 10^{10}$	$3.128\,2 \times 10^{11}$

(e) If everyone consumed at the rate of the USA, then fossil fuel range would be

$$\frac{\text{fossil fuel reserves}}{\text{USA per capita annual consumption} \times \text{world population}} = 26 \text{ years}$$

(f) If all this energy were to be supplied by nuclear and hydroelectricity, dividing demand (the divisor above) by current nuclear and hydroelectricity capacity shows that 47 times current capacity is required. (This assumes that generating capacity equals consumption rate, which is not strictly correct.)

(g) A number of possible assumptions and shortcomings are listed below:

- energy may be imported or exported
- oil (and gas and coal) are used for other products besides energy.
- we assumed 100% conversion efficiency – making town gas from coal only achieved about 25% efficiency
- we assumed zero energy costs of redistributing energy
- we have considered no new technology
- we have ignored new finds
- we have neglected alternatives and biofuels, such as wood, dung, etc.

- as fuels become scarce, price rises will cause more resources to become reserves – economically worthwhile to extract
- we have assumed zero population growth
- we have assumed zero rise in per capita energy consumption, except in (d).

(h) You might have concluded the following:

- the American way of life is probably not sustainable for the whole world unless a huge expansion in fossil reserves occurs, or alternatives, including nuclear and conservation technologies, take off
- there is a huge inequality in consumption
- there is an inequality in disposition of reserves: the trade in energy may become more and more important
- most reserves have short ranges
- the UK and USA are probably importing a lot of fuel.

We have discovered so far that there are at least two good reasons to try to make our fuels go further. First, although there is an abundance of various fuels in the ground, these resources are finite and are not always in the most convenient form. Second, fuel consumption produces pollution. A further incentive can be added: we can save money! Unfortunately, the initial investment in equipment to save fuel and energy can be costly, so careful calculations have to be undertaken before spending money on equipment that will have little value when it wears out.

In this section, we will first explore some aspects of how energy is extracted from fuel and distributed, and then we will think about how these processes can be improved. We will round off the section by looking at waste disposal policy.

READY TO STUDY TEST

Before you begin this section you should be able to:

- describe the difference between temperature and thermal energy
- state the SI unit of temperature
- convert temperatures from celsius to kelvin and vice versa
- calculate efficiencies (look back at Section 2 if you need to)
- relate the rate of heat dissipation by a resistor to current, I, and resistance, R
- state the relationship between power, P, potential difference, V, and current, I.

QUESTIONS

R1 (a) Explain, using the examples of a lukewarm bath of water and a scalding hot cup of tea, the difference between thermal energy and temperature.

(b) What is the SI unit of temperature?

R2 (a) What are the two scientific scales of temperature?

(b) How are temperatures converted between these two scales? Give your answer in the form of formulae and graphs, one scale to appear on your x-axis and one on your y-axis. Show and name fixed points on your graph.

R3 In 1994, 309 123 GW h of electricity was produced by power stations but only 284 439 GW h reached its destination. How efficient is the electricity distribution system and where did the difference in energies go?

R4 A power station is to serve a factory requiring 66 kW. Cables with a total of 10 ohms resistance connect the two and the power can be transmitted so that the voltage at the factory is at either (i) 440 V or (ii) 11 kV.

(a) At what currents would the two systems operate?

(b) What rate of energy loss from the cables would occur in each case?

(c) At what efficiency would power transmission occur in each system?

3.1 Energy destinations

To be able to offer conservation strategies, we need to know *how* energy is used and where it comes from. Figure 3.1 shows the proportion of energy used by different groups in the UK, and Figure 3.2 shows the contribution of various energy sources to the generation of electricity.

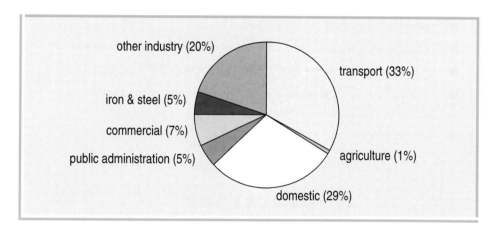

Figure 3.1 Energy consumption by final user in the UK (1994)

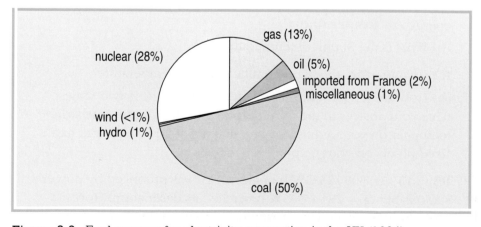

Figure 3.2 Fuel sources for electricity generation in the UK (1994)

Table 3.1 Amount of energy consumed for each fuel source by final user in the UK in 1994/10^{15} J

	Iron and steel	Other industry	Transport	Domestic	Public Admin and Commerce	Agriculture	Total
Coal and coal products*	212.58	163.62	0.00	149.48	23.29	0.40	549.37
Natural gas	73.18	439.23	0.00	1186.96	330.30	4.42	2034.09
Electricity	35.40	316.88	25.68†	362.32	284.27	14.14	1038.69
Petroleum	38.66	322.36	1936.61	116.64	138.97	34.34	2587.58
Solid renewable‡	0.00	2.53	0.00	11.34	2.07	2.20	18.14
Gas renewable‡	0.00	0.70	0.00	0.00	2.19	0.00	2.98
Solar and geothermal	0.00	0.00	0.00	0.42	0.00	0.00	0.42
Total	359.82	1245.41	1962.29	1827.16	781.09	55.5	6231.27

* Approximate values.　　　　† Includes premises.　　　　‡ Calorific values used are estimates.

The fuel industries themselves consumed 4.84×10^{15} J coal and coke, 16.34×10^{15} J petroleum and 6.43×10^{15} J other forms.

Source: *Digest of UK Energy Statistics.*

 What proportion of UK energy consumption occurs in the home?

Figure 3.1 shows that 29% of the fuel used in the UK is used in the home.

 What is the major source of domestic energy?

Table 3.1 indicates that natural gas is the major source of domestic energy.

As you can see, domestic energy conservation is potentially very important.

 What is the highest consumer of energy?

From Figure 3.1 and Table 3.1, you can see that transport is the highest.

Furthermore, most energy is consumed by road transport and most road users are in private cars. So the greatest single consumer of energy in the UK is the public: you and I. Our lifestyles and habits account for around half the total energy consumption for the whole country. We will consider transport in later sections.

3.2 Power generation

Improving power station efficiencies

Figure 3.3 shows approximately how efficiently energy can be transferred from one form to another. You might assume that the law of **conservation of energy** implies that all transfers are 100% efficient, i.e. that we can direct all of our source energy into a single output energy. But the processes of transfer don't work like that. A single input energy always transfers into more than one output, only one of these outputs is likely to be useful. The definition of efficiency involves *useful* energy output.

 If the transfer of thermal energy to mechanical energy is 30% efficient, what percentage of the fuel is lost elsewhere?

$(100 - 30)\% = 70\%$

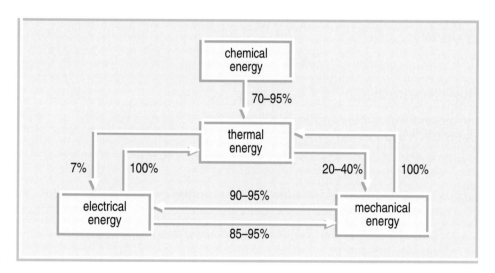

Figure 3.3
Transfer efficiencies

It is not always possible to transfer energy from an available source into the required useful energy in a single step. This, of course, causes even greater losses, as each stage operates under its own efficiency limits.

Worked example: combining efficiencies in complicated processes

In Figure 3.3, a chemical to thermal change is followed by a thermal to mechanical change. What is the overall efficiency? (For this example, we will use the maximum value given in each range.)

Remember that by definition

useful energy output = efficiency × useful energy input to process

Suppose 100 units of energy are transferred. Using the value given in Figure 3.3, 95% efficiency in transferring chemical to thermal energy suggests that 95 units are usefully transferred while 5% are not. The thermal to mechanical process is 40% efficient, so 40% of these 95 units are usefully transferred into mechanical energy; 40% of 95 is 38 units.

Now for two helpful tips: first, a **Sankey diagram** of this may help. In this sort of diagram, percentage energy flows are shown as pathways in which the width of the pathway is proportional to the amount of flow (see Figure 3.4). Notice how 5% is lost from the system at the first stage, and what is left is divided into useful and useless paths at the next stage.

The second tip is to use values of efficiency between 0 and 1 rather than percentages: 0.95 is usefully converted at stage 1 and 0.40 of this at stage 2, leaving $0.95 \times 0.40 = 0.38$, or 38%, at the output. This technique can be extended to more than two stages. ◆

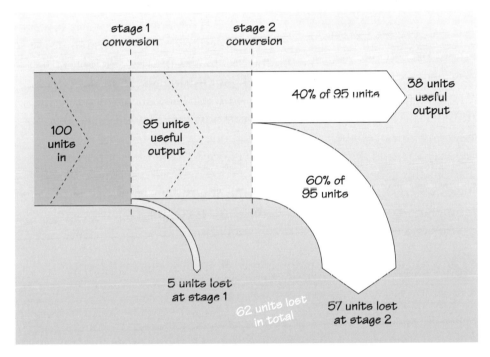

Figure 3.4
A Sankey diagram for energy conversions

Q1   A thermal power station involves transfers from chemical energy to thermal energy, thermal energy to mechanical energy, and then mechanical energy to electrical energy. Work out the overall efficiency using maximum values from Figure 3.3 and techniques from the worked example above. ◆

 Look at Figure 3.3. Which is the least efficient process?

Direct conversion from thermal to electrical energy. (This data is for thermocouple devices – fuel cells may considerably exceed this value.)

A thermal power station

Thermal power stations

Thermal power stations work by burning a fuel in a boiler that creates steam at high pressure. This steam expands against the blades of a turbine, which turns an **alternator** – an a.c. generator. After the steam leaves the turbine, it is condensed and returns to be heated in the boiler again. One reason not to let the water escape is that it is very pure, and using pure water reduces corrosion of the pipework and blades. More importantly, condensing the water lowers the pressure on the downstream side of the turbine and makes it more efficient. Losses from the turbine are by far the biggest sources of inefficiency in thermal power stations. They occur because turbines are limited by the laws of thermodynamics, which state that no heat engine can convert all the thermal energy supplied to it into mechanical (and therefore electrical) energy. In the case of power stations this is because the thermal exhaust must be discharged to the biosphere (usually a river estuary or the atmosphere) at some temperature considerably above **absolute zero**. The exhaust therefore possesses a large amount of thermal energy.

 What sort of power station is not affected by this inefficiency?

A hydroelectric power station.

This constraint does apply to nuclear power stations, since they employ heat engines in the form of steam turbines to drive generators; however, fossil fuel power stations also discharge heat in the form of exhaust **flue gases** (the mixture of combustion products, all containing thermal energy, from the furnace that fuels the boiler). In 1824, Nicholas Carnot, a French military engineer, proposed that the maximum possible efficiency, ε, of heat to mechanical conversion is given by

$$\varepsilon = 1 - \frac{T_2}{T_1}$$

where T_1 and T_2 are inlet and outlet temperatures of the heat engine (measured in kelvin). The upper limit for T_1 depends on the material scientists', especially metallurgists', ability to design efficient materials and machinery, and T_2 is limited by the immediate environment. (*Note:* ε is here given as a fraction between 0 and 1 and is known as the **Carnot efficiency**.)

Figure 3.5 is a Sankey diagram for a heat engine. From the law of conservation of energy, $Q_{high} = W + Q_{low}$, where Q_{high} is the heat in at temperature T_{high}, Q_{low} is the heat out at temperature T_{low}, and W is the work out.

The Carnot efficiency of the engine is given by

$$\varepsilon = \frac{\text{useful work out}}{\text{energy supplied}}$$

So

$$\varepsilon = \frac{W}{Q_{high}}$$

$$= \frac{Q_{high} - Q_{low}}{Q_{high}}$$

$$= 1 - \frac{Q_{low}}{Q_{high}}$$

Carnot was able to show that

$$\frac{Q_{low}}{Q_{high}} = \frac{T_{low}}{T_{high}}$$

for maximum efficiency.

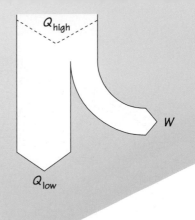

Figure 3.5
A Sankey diagram for a heat engine

 What is the Carnot efficiency, ε, of a turbine running with an inlet temperature of 350°C and an outlet temperature of 110°C?

$$\varepsilon = 1 - \frac{T_2}{T_1}$$

$$= 1 - \frac{(110 + 273\,\text{K})}{(350 + 273\,\text{K})}$$

$$= 0.39$$

 What is the Carnot efficiency, ε, if the outlet temperature is lowered to 80°C?

$$\varepsilon = 1 - \frac{T_2}{T_1}$$

$$= 1 - \frac{(80 + 273\,\text{K})}{(350 + 273\,\text{K})}$$

$$= 0.43$$

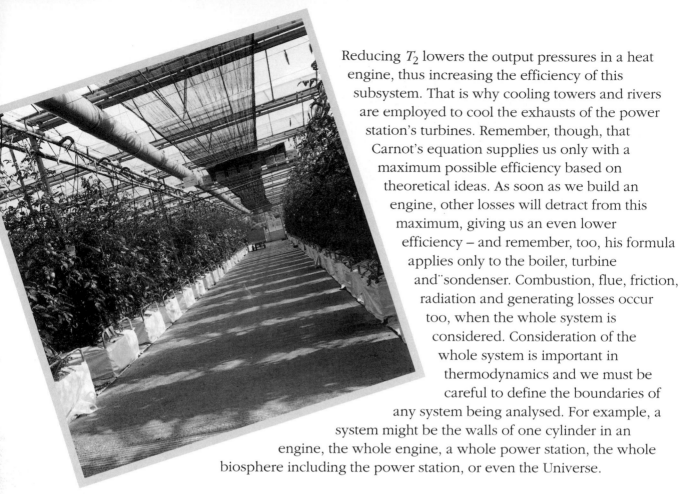

Reducing T_2 lowers the output pressures in a heat engine, thus increasing the efficiency of this subsystem. That is why cooling towers and rivers are employed to cool the exhausts of the power station's turbines. Remember, though, that Carnot's equation supplies us only with a maximum possible efficiency based on theoretical ideas. As soon as we build an engine, other losses will detract from this maximum, giving us an even lower efficiency – and remember, too, his formula applies only to the boiler, turbine and"sondenser. Combustion, flue, friction, radiation and generating losses occur too, when the whole system is considered. Consideration of the whole system is important in thermodynamics and we must be careful to define the boundaries of any system being analysed. For example, a system might be the walls of one cylinder in an engine, the whole engine, a whole power station, the whole biosphere including the power station, or even the Universe.

Tomatoes growing at Drax B

Cogeneration

Cogeneration (also known as **combined heat and power** or **CHP**) power stations aim to exploit waste heat produced by electrical power generation as a useful by-product – using it in an industrial or agricultural process, or for domestic heating. Drax B power station in Yorkshire, for example, has run a sideline growing hothouse tomatoes for many years. In fact, Drax wastes enough heat for all the hothouses in the UK!

Unfortunately, such power stations require the outlet temperature of the turbines to be raised otherwise the thermal energy released can be at too low a temperature to be useful.

 Using the Carnot equation, what effect will raising the outlet temperature have on overall generating efficiency?

If T_2 rises, ε becomes smaller, so electricity generation efficiencies are reduced.

Another potential destination for such energy is **district heating**. In this, heat for buildings and homes is produced centrally, with a heat grid making connections (see Figure 3.6).

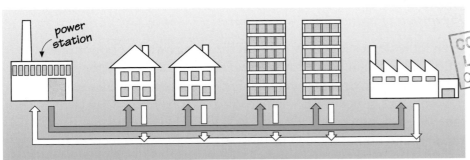

Figure 3.6
How a district heating system is organized

04 6119

COLEG LLANDRILLO COLLEGE
LIBRARY RESOURCE CENTRE
CANOLFAN ADNODDAU LLYFRGELL

Bloom Street power station in Manchester formed part of an early CHP district heating scheme in Britain in 1911. The converted power station generated electricity until 1952 and still produces heat (but not electricity) to this day. Battersea power station in London, until reduced to a sad shell, heated 11 000 homes as well as providing electricity. There are currently no CHP *district* heating schemes operating in the UK.

Q2 Compare the efficiency of a gas-fired power station that generates electricity that heats homes with the 80% efficiency that can be achieved when heating homes by burning gas in the home. (Use maximum values from Figure 3.3 and the answers from R3 and Question 1.) ◆

Q3 Thanks to CHP in the Swedish city of Linköping, 50 000 homes are connected to a district heating system. The Sankey diagram in Figure 3.7 shows the result.

(a) What is the overall efficiency of this CHP plant?

(b) What would its efficiency be if it were supplying only electricity?

(c) Compare your answers with those for Question 2 and write down your conclusions. (*Note:* The figures in this question ignore any **transmission losses** between the CHP station and the city.) ◆

Battersea power station

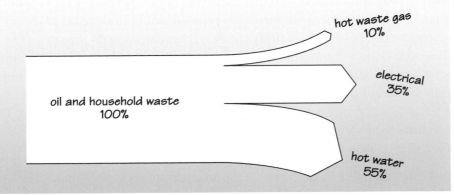

Figure 3.7
Sankey diagram for Question 3

Expansion of industrial cogeneration

Even if the domestic supply sector is throwing away an opportunity for efficiency gains, industry is not. Here, although the scope for cogeneration expansion is very dependent on temperature demands, the government's target of 5 GW of electrical capacity from CHP (with at least the same heat output) by the year 2000 looks likely to be met. 1994 capacity and output is given in Table 3.2.

Table 3.2 Capacity and output from CHP in the UK in 1994

	Capacity/GW	Output/GW h
Electricity	3.140 8	12 152.0
Heat	14.930 7	57 368.3

Q4 What does the total output represent as a fraction of the UK's consumption? Use Table 3.1 and ignore domestic and transport. ◆

Mini- or **micro-CHP** systems (also known as 'minichips' or μCHP), whose generators are often driven by car engines modified to run on gas, are now available and are ideal for use in colleges, hotels and community housing schemes. By 1986, around 200 of these plants were known to be installed in the UK. For example, at 90% total efficiency, one system produces 134 kW of electricity and 267 kW of heat.

Q5 A nuclear power station supplies 2.0 GW of electricity only and costs £2500M. A minichip system costs £7875 and can supply 15 kW of electricity and 38 kW of heat. What is the cost of each installation per kW of (a) electricity, (b) electricity and useful heat output? ◆

Dependence on local supplies such as minichips would reduce transmission losses (heat loss from cables, transformer losses, etc.), though perhaps at the expense of energy used in fuel delivery.

Potential for minichips

The installation of these CHP units in all suitable large buildings in the UK would create about 1 GW of electrical capacity. Minichip units could also supply heat and electricity to domestic dwellings. Several homes could share a single engine, with insulated pipes running underground to distribute the hot water. A study by the Open University's Energy Research Group shows that a system producing 40 kW of electricity could also heat about 50 homes, saving each house about £90 per year in fuel bills at current prices. There are some 24 million dwellings in the UK. Allocating each one a 1 kW share in a CHP plant would create an electrical generating capacity of 24 GW. In 1994, around 86 GW of electricity was centrally generated.

It is often said that large power stations generate electricity more efficiently than thousands of small machines. However, a true comparison must include capital costs: as we saw in Question 5, minichips cost around £525 per kW of electricity output, which is slightly less than a coal-fired power station; nuclear stations cost around £1000 to £1500 per kW output. The precise cost of nuclear-generated electricity depends largely on the rate of interest charged on capital investment and the costs of decommissioning.

It has even been proposed that cars themselves should also act as minichip plants: after all, we already use the engine to heat the car. If when the car was in the garage its engine was used to drive a generator, then it could supply electricity to the house from its alternator with additional heat from its exhaust and hot water from its cooling system, thereby reducing overall use of coal and gas and individuals' electricity and domestic fuel bills.

 What disadvantages do you foresee?

> Disadvantages might include noise and vibration, shortened engine life, increased use of oil and more expensive cars.

Questions 6 and 7 look at the conversion of orthodox power stations to combined heat and power and district heating.

Q6 An orthodox thermal power station works at 40% generating efficiency and operates between temperatures of 560 K and 280 K. The transmission efficiency to the city it serves is 95%.

(a) How efficient ought the system to be according to Carnot?

(b) Compare your answer with the actual generating efficiency. What percentage of the energy in the fuel is lost in other ways?

(c) Assume that this fractional loss remains the same, but the turbine exhaust is increased to 380K, 60% of the waste heat is extracted for a district heating scheme, but 20% of this is lost during distribution. How efficient overall is the power station *and* distribution system (i) before conversion, (ii) after conversion to CHP district heating? ◆

Q7 A district heating scheme rated at 4.0 MW uses water at 90°C, returning it at 30°C. What mass of water per second transfers energy at this rate? ◆

Q8 How does the maximum output of a petrol station compare with the output of a 1 GW power station in watts? Assume eight pumps deliver 30 litres each every four minutes. (Take the calorific value of petrol as 43.2 MJ kg^{-1} and the density of petrol as 680 kg m^{-3}.) ◆

From your answer to Question 6, you can see that CHP stations could supply about as much thermal energy as electricity – nearly equal to the domestic demand for thermal energy (given in Table 3.1). So why hasn't cogeneration and district heating really taken off? Interest *has* re-awakened in the USA, while mainland Europe continues to supply cities and populations considered by the UK to be too remote to service; for example, more than 25% of Denmark's heating requirement is met by CHP. Some say that our variable climate in the UK causes swings in heat demand and inefficient running during short periods of the year. If the primary cogeneration fuel had been coal, jobs would have been saved, with no net rise in CO_2 or SO_2 discharges and installation of city-based CHP could create around 300 000 jobs. If the primary fuel were nuclear, CO_2 emissions could be cut at a stroke but there would be concern over waste disposal and the siting of nuclear plant near towns. (Some people believe the waste itself should fuel district heat with its **radioactive decay energy**!)

We have shown that a combined heat and power plant should be more efficient than any dedicated electricity supply plant and can be more efficient than heat-only production. Drawbacks of CHP are that it can be noisy, it is a long-term investment and district heat pipelines have to be paid for. Industry can install CHP partly because it can rely on the back-up power of the **National Grid**.

Much research continues to be directed at improving electrical efficiency alone, even though CHP has been shown to work, because the electricity generating boards had a responsibility to concentrate on generation. Unfortunately, as we calculated earlier, the need in CHP to extract steam at a higher temperature reduces generating efficiency slightly and the old Central Electricity Generating Board (CEGB) mandate required it to supply electricity at as low a price as possible. To this end, larger, easily serviced power stations were located remotely, securing economies of scale, so there was no means of marketing their waste heat. Following the privatization of electricity production and the break up of the CEGB, companies have taken part in the '**dash for gas**': they have ignored the attractions of cogeneration, with its associated investment costs, and instead have focused on building gas-fired plant that produce only electricity, which increases their short-term profits and helps to meet the UK's CO_2 emission reduction targets.

3.3 Energy from waste

In Britain, not only do we convert energy inefficiently and often use it frivolously, we also allow vast amounts of potentially valuable resources to pour into the atmosphere, rivers and seas, and to be buried in disused quarries. Often, this waste has material as well as fuel value. The UK produces waste with an energy equivalent of about 8.4×10^{17} J per year. Much of it is disposed of in landfill sites (which are continually filling up and so available space is getting less) or by incineration – gas *may* be extracted from the former, the latter may produce useful heat.

Each year, Britain discharges over its land and sea many millions of tonnes of sewage and effluent. In theory, energy equivalent to that provided by about eight power stations could be produced from animal waste alone. There is potential for plant waste to be turned into **biogas** (mostly methane and carbon dioxide, produced by bacterial fermentation or anaerobic digestion of organic matter). A by-product of turning such waste into gas would be an excellent fertilizer. Gas from waste can, of course, deliver district heating

 What are the disadvantages and advantages of such schemes?

Unless centrally organized with an effective system of pipelines etc. installed, biogas production would be devolved, requiring plant at each place of production. Recycling may save extraction and refining costs but it could attract sorting, storage and transport costs, and there would be the possibility of pollution during re-manufacture.

Incineration is often seen as the best solution to waste disposal, and it could provide a net energy output, but it has its own pollution problems. Landfill digestion has problems of liquid seepage and biogas emission, leading many to consider it the worst form of disposal. Ironically, some landfill 'waste' is now considered to be so valuable that it is being mined. It is clearly best not to make waste in the first place!

UK electricity and heat supply in 1994 from renewable sources, including wind, hydroelectric power, landfill gas, sewage digestion and straw and waste combustion totalled 6.11×10^{16} J, less than 1% of all energy consumption.

In some respects, industry has been rather more active in energy conservation than have domestic users. This may reflect more stringent financial controls – money spent needlessly on industry running costs eats into profits, but homes are often not owned for long enough for savings to be made.

However, investing in energy saving costs money too. Some energy management consultancy firms are beginning to lease equipment, or even loan it free of charge, in exchange for a share of the savings. In the USA, some power generating companies do this on a domestic scale. So far such schemes have not evolved in the UK.

 Exploration 3.1   A research exercise

Using the library and by approaching appropriate bodies, e.g. ETSU, Harwell, Oxfordshire, OX11 0RA (tel: 01235 432 450), Milton Keynes Recycling Centre (tel: 01908 225004), try to evaluate the scope for energy conservation by the measures outlined above and waste recycling in the UK. Mention (and try to quantify) other benefits. Your answer should include: cogeneration, district heat, electric transport (and heat spin-off), animal waste processing, domestic and industrial waste incineration or landfill gas production. (*Note:* Remember that some electricity generation is not thermal.)

Achievements

After working through this section you should be able to:

- recall the different ranges of efficiency of energy conversion
- use the Carnot efficiency equation
- construct and use Sankey diagrams
- explain the potential efficiency of cogeneration (or CHP)
- list some ways waste can be turned into useful energy.

Glossary

Absolute zero The temperature at which matter possess no thermal energy. It is the lowest possible temperature (0 K on the absolute, or Kelvin, scale; equivalent to $-273.15°C$ on the Celsius scale).

Alternator A machine whose shaft is driven by an engine or turbine and converts mechanical energy into alternating current electricity. More usually called a generator.

Biogas Gas from a biological origin, e.g. methane from compost.

Carnot efficiency, ε The maximum theoretical efficiency of a heat engine given by $\varepsilon = 1 - \dfrac{T_2}{T_1}$, where T_1 and T_2 are the inlet and outlet temperatures of the heat engine.

Combined heat and power (CHP) A system designed to generate electrical power and also use the 'waste' heat from the process for other industrial, agricultural or domestic purposes.

Conservation of energy Energy cannot be created or destroyed, it can only be transferred from one form to another. The processes of working or heating simply transfer it.

Dash for gas The short-term policy of building gas-fired, combined cycle power stations to replace coal-fired ones, both for rapid profits and to meet the UK's CO_2 emission reduction targets. Combined cycle power stations employ a highly efficient power station cycle in which a gas turbine exhaust raises steam that also drives a turbine; both turbines power electricity generators. They can be combined heat and power too. Such power stations are more efficient than coal-fired ones and produce less CO_2 per joule output, but they use precious resources of gas that could conveniently be piped direct to homes and industry where it could be used even more efficiently for heating.

District heating A single heating, and possibly hot water, system serving a large number of properties in an area. Such a heating system can be run from a CHP power station, which also produces electricity.

Flue gases Waste gases from a heating process.

Mini- or micro-CHP Small-scale power plant supplying electrical and thermal energy from generators, exhaust and heat exchangers.

National Grid The network of high-voltage power cables linking power stations to provide the national power supply.

Radioactive decay energy The energy emitted during the process of radioactive decay, i.e. the emission of alpha, beta or gamma radiation.

Sankey diagram A diagram demonstrating graphically and in true proportion the energy flows in a system, starting with the energy sources and showing losses, heat exchange loops, etc., to the degree desired. Named after its originator, Richard Sankey, an Irish military engineer.

Transmission losses Energy losses in the power cables between the power station and the end user.

Answers to Ready to Study test

R1

(a) The cup of tea is hotter (at a higher temperature) but the greater volume of the bath water contains more thermal energy.

(b) The kelvin.

R2

(a) The two scales are celsius and kelvin.

(b) The two scales have the same unit size but different fixed points, most notably $0\,K = -273°C$. You can convert a temperature given on one scale to a temperature on the other using the formulae

$$T = \theta + 273$$

or

$$\theta = T - 273$$

where T is the temperature in kelvin and θ is the temperature in celsius.

Figure 3.8 shows a conversion graph.

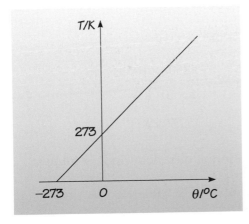

Figure 3.8 Graph of temperature in kelvin against temperature in degrees celsius

R3

$$\text{Efficiency of system} = \frac{\text{useful energy output}}{\text{total energy input}} \times 100\%$$

$$= \frac{284\,439\,\text{GW h}}{309\,123\,\text{GW h}} \times 100\%$$

$$= 92\%$$

(to 2 significant figures)

The energy losses in transmission were due mainly to the thermal energy dissipated by the power cables and transformers.

R4

(a) Power $= IV$

therefore

$$I = \frac{\text{power}}{V}$$

(i) For transmission at 440 V, current flow into the factory and along transmission cables is given by

$$I = \frac{66 \times 10^3 \text{ W}}{440 \text{ V}}$$

$$= 150\,\text{A}$$

(ii) For transmission at 11 kV

$$I = \frac{66 \times 10^3 \text{ W}}{11 \times 10^3 \text{ V}}$$

$$= 6.0\,\text{A}$$

(b) Rate of heat loss $= I^2 R$

(i) For transmission at 440 V

$$\text{rate of heat loss} = 150^2 \text{ A}^2 \times 10\,\Omega$$

$$= 225\,\text{kW}$$

(ii) For transmission at 11 kV

$$\text{rate of heat loss} = 6.0^2 \text{ A}^2 \times 10\,\Omega$$

$$= 360\,\text{W}$$

(c) Efficiency $= \dfrac{\text{useful power output}}{\text{total power input}} \times 100\%$

(i) For transmission at 440 V

$$\text{efficiency} = \frac{66\,\text{kW}}{66\,\text{kW} + 225\,\text{kW}} \times 100\%$$

$$= 23\% \text{ (to two significant figures)}$$

(ii) For transmission at 11 kV

$$\text{efficiency} = \frac{66\,\text{kW}}{66\,\text{kW} + 0.36\,\text{kW}} \times 100\%$$

$$= 99\% \text{ (to two significant figures)}$$

Answers to questions in the text

Q1

Efficiencies are 95%, 40% and 95%, respectively

$0.95 \times 0.40 \times 0.95 = 0.361$ or 36.1%

Q2

From Question 1, the efficiency of transferring chemical energy to electrical energy is 36.1%.

From R3, the efficiency of electrical distribution 92%.

From Figure 3.3, the efficiency of electrical heating is 100%.

Combining these gives

$0.361 \times 0.92 \times 1.00 = 0.33$ or 33%

Neglecting pipeline losses, gas heating is 80% efficient, so burning gas directly in the home is much more efficient.

Q3

(a) Overall efficiency is 90%.

(b) It would be just 35% efficient if it were supplying only electricity.

(c) An efficiency of 90% is better than supplying gas directly to the houses and a great improvement on using electricity for heating homes.

Q4

From Table 3.1,

UK annual consumption $= 2442 \times 10^{15}$ J

$$= 6.92 \times 10^{11}\,\text{kW h}$$

$$= 692\,000\,\text{GW h}$$

From Table 3.2, total output is 69 520.3 GW h

$$\frac{69\,520.3\,\text{GW h}}{678\,000\,\text{GW h}} = 0.10 \text{ or } 10\%$$

(to two significant figures)

Q5

(a) Considering electricity output only:

Minichip

$$\text{cost per kW} = \frac{£7875}{15\,\text{kW}}$$

$$= £525\,\text{kW}^{-1}$$

Power station

$$\text{cost per kW} = \frac{£2500 \times 10^6}{2 \times 10^6\,\text{kW}}$$

$$= £1250\,\text{kW}^{-1}$$

(b) Considering electricity and useful heat output:

Minichip

$$\text{cost per kW} = \frac{£7875}{53\,\text{kW}}$$

$$= £149\,\text{kW}^{-1}$$

Power station

The power station produces no useful heat, so

$$\text{cost per kW} = £1250\,\text{kW}^{-1}$$

Q6

(a) Carnot efficiency is

$$\varepsilon = 1 - \frac{T_2}{T_1}$$

$$= \left(1 - \frac{280\,\text{K}}{560\,\text{K}}\right)$$

$$= 0.5 \text{ or } 50\%$$

(b) The practical efficiency of the power stations is 40%, so one-fifth of 50%, (i.e. 10%) is lost in other ways.

(c) (i) The Carnot efficiency is now

$$\left(1 - \frac{380}{560}\right) \times 100\% = 32\%$$

One-fifth is lost as before in the power station, leaving 25.6%. 95% of this, i.e.

$$0.95 \times 0.256 = 0.243 \text{ or } 24.3\%$$

arrives at the city.

(ii) Waste heat recovered is 60% of $(100 - 25.6)\%$, i.e.

$$0.60 \times (1.000 - 0.256) = 0.446 \text{ or } 44.6\%$$

but 20% of this is lost in distribution, so

$$0.80 \times 0.446 = 0.357 \text{ or } 35.7\%$$

arrives at the destination.

Overall, then, 24.3% of original fuel arrives as electricity and 35.7% as heat, making 60.0% total.

The original overall efficiency for just electricity was

$$0.95 \times 0.40 = 0.38 \text{ or } 38\% \text{ efficiency.}$$

Q7

$$Q = Mc\Delta\theta$$

where Q is energy supplied per second, M is the mass of water flowing per second, c is the specific heat of water, and $\Delta\theta$ is the temperature difference in kelvin.

$$Q = 4.0\,\text{MW}$$
$$= 4.0 \times 10^6 \,\text{J s}^{-1}$$
$$c = 4200\,\text{J kg}^{-1}\,\text{K}^{-1}$$
$$\Delta\theta = 60\,\text{K}$$

so

$$4.0 \times 10^6\,\text{J s}^{-1} = M \times 4200\,\text{J kg}^{-1}\,\text{K}^{-1} \times 60\,\text{K}$$

Therefore

$$M = \frac{4.0 \times 10^6\,\text{J s}^{-1}}{4200\,\text{J kg}^{-1}\text{K}^{-1} \times 60\,\text{K}}$$

$$= 15.873\,\text{kg s}^{-1}$$

$$= 16\,\text{kg s}^{-1} \text{ (to two significant figures)}$$

Q8

Volume of output of pumps per second

$$= \frac{8 \times 30\,\text{litre}}{4 \times 60\,\text{s}}$$

$$= \frac{240\,\text{litre}}{240\,\text{s}}$$

$$= 1\,\text{litre s}^{-1}$$

$$= 1 \times 10^{-3}\,\text{m}^3\,\text{s}^{-1}$$

Mass of output per second

$$= \text{density} \times \text{volume}$$

$$= 680\,\text{kg m}^{-3} \times 10^{-3}\,\text{m}^3\,\text{s}^{-1}$$

$$= 0.68\,\text{kg s}^{-1}$$

From Section 2, recall that energy output = calorific value × mass

Energy output per second

$$= 0.68 \, \text{kg s}^{-1} \times 43.2 \, \text{MJ kg}^{-1}$$

$$= 29.4 \, \text{MJ s}^{-1}$$

$$= 30 \, \text{MW}$$

(to two significant figures)

So the output of approximately 30 such garages compares to the output of one 1 GW power station.

4

One key feature of modern life is mobility. Thanks to passenger jet aircraft we can now travel to distant parts of the Earth within a day when it once took weeks by land and sea. Perhaps more significantly, the car is shaping everything around us. Our cities have been re-designed for the car – ring-roads, by-passes, flyovers, roundabouts, car parks, park-and-rides and out-of-town shopping centres have all been built to accommodate the car. And the countryside is sliced through by motorways. These changes have been taking place since Henry Ford's company produced the Model T Ford – the first mass-produced car.

The Model T Ford was introduced in 1908 and was an immediate success. It was designed to last and to be economical. It had a four-cylinder internal combustion engine. It was so popular that the Ford Motor Company had to mass produce it on a moving assembly line from 1914 onwards. Mass production reduced the cost – much in the way that the price of computers and other electronic goods often goes down today. In 1908 the car cost about $850, but in 1925 it sold for just $290.

In 1919, 50% of all the cars in the world were Model T Fords. It was ideal for its time: it could be used on rough country roads and it was simple to drive and to maintain. More than 15 million had been made by the time it was superseded by other models and production stopped on 31 May 1927.

Model T Ford

THE IMPACT OF THE CAR ON THE ENVIRONMENT

Even our attitudes have changed because of the mobility that our cars provide – we drive instead of catching the bus or walking. In the 1950s and 1960s 'going for a drive' became a recreational activity in its own right for some people. Figure 4.1 shows how the relative use of different types of passenger transport changed between 1950 and 1990.

Using a car is so much part of many of our lives that we can't imagine how we could manage without one.

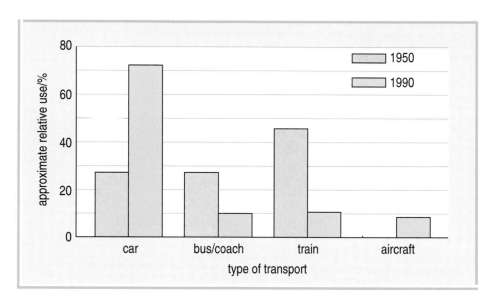

Figure 4.1 Relative use of different types of passenger transport

You will discover in this section that our dependence upon the car is a serious threat to the environment. This is because the number of motor vehicles in the world has grown ever since the introduction of the Model T and is continuing to grow. Cars produce waste and a number of different pollutants when they are being driven. The exhaust contains carbon monoxide, carbon dioxide, water vapour, nitrogen oxides, lead compounds and hydrocarbons. Carbon dioxide and nitrogen oxides are heat-retaining gases that contribute to the greenhouse effect. Nitrogen oxides are also responsible for some depletion of the ozone layer. The pollution is on a scale that is beyond Earth's natural capacity to absorb. Technology exists, and is being developed, to reduce the pollution, so perhaps the damage to the environment can be reduced.

We will first try to get a picture of the extent of the problem – how many cars there are and the rate at which this number is growing, and the contribution that cars are actually making to pollution of the planet. Then we will look at how a car engine works and how the environmental impact of cars can be minimized.

READY TO STUDY TEST

Before you begin this section you should be able to:

- plot graphs from appropriate data and work out the gradient and intercept of straight-line graphs
- generate tables of theoretical data from an algebraic relationship between given quantities
- multiply and divide powers of ten (and other base numbers)
- recall and use the relationship density = mass/volume
- recall and use the relationship pressure = force/area
- state and apply the law of conservation of energy
- calculate efficiencies, given appropriate information
- show some understanding of the significance of absolute temperature and know its unit
- calculate the amount of energy required to raise the temperature of a body by a certain amount given its mass and specific heat capacity.

QUESTIONS

R1 A graph of distance against time is a straight line with a gradient of 5.00 m s^{-1} and an intercept of 8.00 m. What is the distance, s, at the following times: (a) 10 s, (b) 100 s?

R2 The relationship between the distance travelled by a car, s, and the time during which it has been accelerating, t, is:

$$s = 0.1\,\text{m s}^{-1}t + 0.2\,\text{m s}^{-2}t^2$$

How far has the car travelled at the following times: (a) 0 s, (b) 1.0 s, (c) 10 s?

R3 What is the volume of a cube that has a mass of 1.0×10^9 kg and is made of a material with a density of 1.0×10^3 kg m^{-3}?

R4 A car with a mass of 1000 kg exerts a pressure of 10 kPa on the ground with one of its four tyres. What is the area of tyre in contact with the ground? (Use $g = 9.81$ m s^{-2}.)

R5 A lump of dough is dropped 30 m. All the gravitational potential energy is eventually transferred through heating. If it is assumed that it is only the dough that is heated and its temperature rises by 0.1 K, what is the specific heat capacity of the dough? (Use $g = 10$ m s^{-2}.)

R6 The temperature of matter in kelvin is a measure of the kinetic energy of its particles (atoms or molecules). What do you call the temperature at which the particles have no kinetic energy?

R7 (a) Explain what is meant by the efficiency of a machine.

(b) If a lifting machine has an efficiency of 75% and uses 240 J of energy, how much potential energy has been gained by the object it has lifted?

4.1 The number of cars in the world

Table 4.1 shows how many motor vehicles there were in the world between 1940 and 1990. If you assume that there were no motor vehicles in 1900, it is possible to work out a mathematical relationship that fits these data. Once you have worked out the relationship you can use it to make predictions about how many vehicles there will be in any year in the future, assuming that the growth continues in the same way. The purpose of the following exploration is to help you to find the mathematical relationship and to make such predictions.

Table 4.1 The number of motor vehicles in the world between 1940 and 1990

Year	Number of motor vehicles/millions
1940	25.6
1950	62.5
1960	129.6
1970	240.1
1980	409.6
1990	656.1

 Exploration 4.1 Predicting future numbers of vehicles

(a) Plot a graph of the data in Table 4.1, use the vertical axis for the number of motor vehicles, in millions, and the horizontal axis for the year.

You should get a curve showing an accelerating growth in the number of motor vehicles in the world. It would be possible to make predictions for the future by extrapolating this curve, but that would really be a matter of guesswork. By using **logarithms** we can find a mathematical relationship between the year and the number of cars. The data in the table are based on real data, but they have been adjusted to make this exercise simpler. The adjusted data take into account the fact that the number of motor vehicles in 1900, before the mass production of the Model T, was very small.

(b) Copy the data into a new table with three extra columns. You can fill in the third column now with the number of years since 1900 – so 1940 becomes 40, 1950 becomes 50, and so on.

(c) This part covers how to use logarithms; if you already know how to use them you might be able to miss it out.

Logarithms are the power to which a certain base number is raised so that the result equals the number you want to represent as a logarithm. If the base is the number '10', for example, then the logarithm of '100' is '2' because $10^2 = 100$. Logarithms with a base of '10' are called common logarithms.

 What are the common logarithms of the following numbers: (a) 0.1, (b) 10, (c) 1000, (d) 1 000 000

(a) –1, (b) 1, (c) 3, (d) 6.

You can probably see that the common logarithm of '1' would be '0'. Any number raised to the power '0' equals '1', so the logarithm of '1' using any base will be '0'.

Numbers between '0.1' and '1.0' will have common logarithms between '–1' and '0', e.g. the common logarithm of '0.5' is '–0.301'. To find the common logarithm of any number you can use your calculator – find the button labelled log or lg.

Use your calculator to find the common logarithms of the following numbers: (a) 0.25, (b) 5.0, (c) 75, (d) 660, (e) 4700.

(a) –0.602, (b) 0.699, (c) 1.875, (d) 2.820, (e) 3.672.

If you multiply 10^2 by 10^4 the result is 10^6, i.e. the powers are added. The same rule must apply if you consider the powers to be the common logarithms, so:

$$\log(10^2 \times 10^4) = \log(10^2) + \log(10^4)$$

This applies in general, so letting A and B represent any two numbers:

$$\log(A \times B) = \log A + \log B \qquad (4.1)$$

If $B = A$, then:

$$\log(A \times B) = \log(A \times A)$$
$$= \log(A^2)$$
$$= \log A + \log A$$
$$= 2\log A$$

i.e. $\log(A^2) = 2\log A$

This also generalizes, letting n represent the power A is raised to (it can be positive or negative, whole or fractional) gives

$$\log(A^n) = n\log A \qquad (4.2)$$

There is another type of logarithms that are often used – these are natural logarithms (also known as Naperian logarithms), which use the number e as their base. You may have come across e in connection with radioactivity or capacitors charging and discharging, e = 2.718 ....

There is also a button for natural logarithms on your calculator, it is labelled ln and the reverse function is e^x.

 Use your calculator to find the natural logarithms of the following numbers: (a) 0.25, (b) 5.0, (c) 75, (d) 660, (e) 4700

(a) –1.386, (b) 1.609, (c) 4.317, (d) 6.492, (e) 8.455.

The same rules apply to natural logarithms that applied to common logarithms, so:

$$\ln(A \times B) = \ln A + \ln B \tag{4.3}$$

and

$$\ln(A^n) = n \ln A \tag{4.4}$$

(d) The general equation for a straight-line graph is:

$$y = mx + c \tag{4.5}$$

where y is the variable plotted on the y-axis, x is the variable plotted on the x-axis and m and c are two constants that fix the line: they are the gradient and the intercept on the y-axis, respectively. See Figure 4.2.

If the gradient and intercept of the graph are known, the value of y can be found for any value of x.

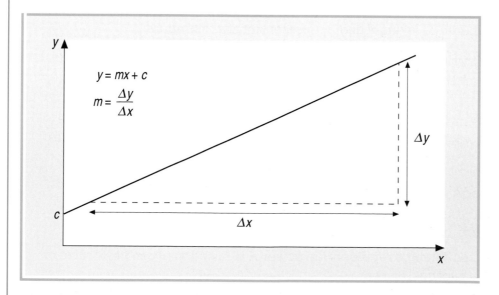

Figure 4.2 The general expression for a straight-line graph

If the equation for a straight-line graph is:

$$y = 0.50x + 5.50$$

find the value of y for the following values of x: (a) 1.00, (b) –1.00, (c) 5.00, (d) –10.0.

(a) 6.00, (b) 5.00, (c) 8.00, (d) 0.50.

Logarithms can be used to manipulate the data for the number of motor vehicles in the world so that it can be plotted to produce a straight-line graph.

Many different relationships can produce a curved graph, one major family of such relationships are called polynomials, e.g.

$$y = kx^n$$

where k and n are constants. Let's assume this type of relationship relates the number of motor vehicles in the world, y, to the number of years since 1900, x. Then the logarithm (let's say natural logarithm) of y is given by

$$\ln y = \ln(kx^n)$$

and applying Equation (4.3) gives

$$\ln y = \ln k + \ln(x^n)$$

Now, by applying Equation (4.4)

$$\ln(x^n) = n\ln x$$

so

$$\ln y = \ln k + n\ln x$$

or

$$\ln y = n\ln x + \ln k$$

In this expression $\ln y$ and $\ln x$ are variables because y and x are variables, n is a constant and $\ln k$ is a constant because k is. This equation is the equation of a straight line if $\ln y$ and $\ln x$ are plotted on the axes of the graph – the intercept on the $\ln y$ axis will be $\ln k$ and the gradient will be n.

(e) Now complete the table with the natural logarithms of the number of years since 1900 in the fourth column (this will be your $\ln x$) and the natural logarithms of the number of motor vehicles in the last column (this will be your $\ln y$).

Plot the graph of $\ln y$ against $\ln x$ ($\ln y$ on the vertical axis and $\ln x$ on the horizontal axis).

Q1   (a) Using your graph, find n (the gradient) and $\ln k$ (the intercept on the vertical axis). From the value for $\ln k$ determine the value of the constant k.

(b) Write down the expression for the number of motor vehicles, y, in terms of the number of years since 1900, x, using the actual values for n and k.

(c) Use this expression to predict the number of motor vehicles in the world in the years 2000 and 2050. ◆

In the USA, there is already almost one car per adult. Most countries have a far lower ratio, so the number of motor vehicles in the world is likely to continue to increase as everyone seeks parity with the USA. UK Department of Transport figures predict that Britain will reach this situation in 2020. If all these cars were parked bumper to bumper they would form a line more than 200 000 miles long. The distance from London to Glasgow is only about 350 miles – imagine a traffic jam on a 572-lane motorway from London to Glasgow! Setting aside the environmental implications of this number of vehicles, the traffic congestion in a densely populated country like Britain would be so bad that increased mobility would become a questionable advantage of car ownership.

4.2 Emissions and waste produced by cars

A typical car in Britain will get through more than 10 tonnes of petrol before it is scrapped and it will produce four times its own mass of carbon dioxide every year. About a billion (1×10^9) tonnes of oil are used annually to power motor vehicles, which produce over 10 000 billion (1×10^{13}) cubic metres of exhaust fumes a year.

Urban smog –
Shanghai, China

These exhaust fumes are carried up into the atmosphere. If they were not, then the fumes from Britain's cars would form a poisonous layer on the ground several metres deep in just one year.

Q2 Assume that 1.00×10^{13} m^3 of exhaust fumes are produced every year and these fumes have the same density as air (1.30 kg m^{-3}). If they then form a layer that has a density of 1000 kg m^{-3}, what would be the thickness of the layer if it were deposited equally over the whole of the Earth? (*Note:* Remember that the surface area of a sphere is $4\pi r^2$, where r is the radius of the sphere. The radius of Earth is 6.40×10^6 m.) ◆

Urban smog, made up largely of clouds of exhaust fumes, has been a problem in several densely populated cities such as Los Angeles, and is still chokingly bad in many other cities of the world, such as Athens, Manila and Bangkok.

The major constituents of motor vehicle exhaust fumes are summarized in Table 4.2.

Table 4.2 The harmful constituents of motor vehicle exhaust

Constituent	Percentage of world emissions* from motor vehicles	Undesirable properties
Carbon dioxide	14% (1.9 kg of CO_2 is produced per litre of petrol)	Contributes to global warming as a greenhouse gas
Carbon monoxide	More than 90% (concentration in lower atmosphere is increasing by about 1% per year)	Poisonous, can cause respiratory disease
Nitrogen oxides	More than 60%	Contribute to acid rain
Hydrocarbons	More than 90%	Cause respiratory disease and possibly cancer
Carbon particles	40% (about 50 times more emitted by diesel engines than by petrol engines)	Cause respiratory disease and possibly cancer. Reduce visibility
Aldehydes	More from diesel engines	Toxic and carcinogenic
Benzene	70%	Carcinogenic
Lead	90%	Toxic
Sulphur oxides	5%	Contribute to acid rain

* Only emissions that result from human activities are considered here.

Many of the figures in Table 4.2 date back to the 1980s; however, they give a clear indication of the importance of reducing the exhaust emissions from motor vehicles.

California has some of the most stringent anti-pollution laws in the world; these have committed the motor industry to reducing pollution by introducing, in stages, cars that produce progressively lower levels of emissions:

■ transitional low-emission vehicles (TLEV), which produce half the emissions of conventional cars, have been on the market since 1994

■ low-emission vehicles (LEV), which produce a quarter of the emissions of conventional cars, followed

■ ultra-low emission vehicles (ULEV), which produce an eighth of the emissions of conventional cars, were introduced in 1997

■ zero-emission vehicles (ZEV) are due to come on to the market in 1998.

Total vehicle emissions have been falling since the 1980s because of such legislation, better engine design and the introduction of **catalytic converters**. However, despite such improvements, the ever-increasing number of cars may cause emissions to start to rise again. Exploration 4.2 is based upon one estimate of the situation.

Exploration 4.2   Estimated levels of hydrocarbons in the global atmosphere

1 HOUR

One estimate of the levels of hydrocarbons in the atmosphere relates annual emissions, h (in millions of tonnes), to the year, t, according to the following relationship:

$$h = 0.034t^2 - 138t + 1.735 \times 10^5$$

(a) Produce a table of data for the years 1980 to 2080.

(b) Plot a graph of the data (h against t).

(c) Estimate the year in which the increasing number of cars outweighs the benefits of the technological and legal measures being used from the 1980s onwards.

4.3   The car engine – how it works

The most commonly used engine for motor vehicles is a four-cylinder, four-stroke petrol engine (a type of **internal combustion engine**). The pistons in the four cylinders are all connected to a crankshaft by connecting rods, so the movement of one piston will move all the other pistons. (See Figure 4.3.)

Each cylinder goes through the same sequence of strokes but not at the same time. When cylinder 1 is performing the *intake stroke* (drawing a mixture of air and fuel vapour in through the inlet valve), cylinder 2 is performing the *compression stroke* (compressing the gas mixture with both valves closed), in cylinder 3 the mixture is being ignited by an electrical discharge from the sparkplug in the *power stroke* (the high pressure produced by the hot gases forces the piston downwards) and

Figure 4.3
The four strokes of a petrol engine

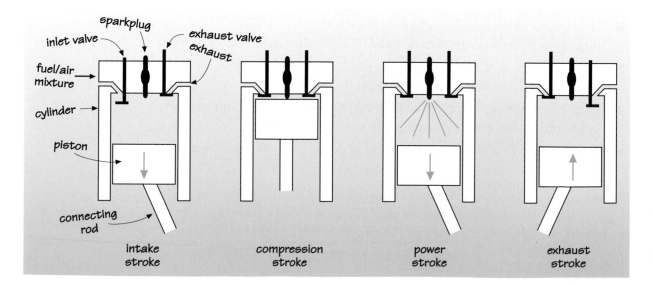

cylinder 4 is in the *exhaust stroke* (the hot gases produced by the combustion of the fuel/air mixture are forced out of the exhaust valve). The power stroke of cylinder 3 provides the energy for the other three cylinders to perform their strokes.

Now cylinder 1 goes into its compression stroke, cylinder 2 into its power stroke, cylinder 3 into its exhaust stroke and cylinder 4 into its intake stroke. So, there is always one cylinder in its power stroke to provide energy for the other cylinders to perform their strokes.

Q3   A car uses 9.0 litres of petrol during a one hour journey. If the engine is running at 2000 revolutions per minute throughout the journey, how much petrol is consumed during each revolution? ◆

Q4   Draw a sketch of a shaft that could be used to connect all the cylinder connecting rods together so that the operation of a four-cylinder four-stroke engine is a continuous process. (This is hard to draw, so don't spend too much time on it.) ◆

Let's look at the energy transferred during each part of the cycle; this requires some knowledge of thermodynamics. Energy can be transferred *into* the gas in two distinct ways: first by heating, Q, and second by working, W. When energy is transferred into the gas, its internal energy will increase by ΔU. This extra internal energy is usually in the form of kinetic energy of the molecules of the gas, in other words the temperature of the gas increases.

$\Delta U = Q + W$

This is known as the **first law of thermodynamics** – it is a statement of the law of conservation of energy, which you met earlier.

If W is transferred into the gas very quickly into the gas, the temperature of the gas will rise because it takes time for energy to be transferred out of the gas by conduction, convection, etc. This is called an **adiabatic change**. As $Q = 0$, $\Delta U = W$.

On the other hand, if W is transferred very slowly it can be balanced by the energy being transferred out of the gas as it heats its surroundings, so $Q + W = 0$ and therefore $\Delta U = 0$. The temperature of the gas cannot change if $\Delta U = 0$. This is called an **isothermal change**.

If Q is transferred into a gas that is in a container of fixed volume, the gas cannot expand, so no energy can be transferred out of the system by it doing work, i.e. $W = 0$, so $\Delta U = Q$. This is an **isovolumetric change**.

In the engine, the gas in the cylinders can expand because the pistons move fairly freely in the cylinder. Ideally, the pressure inside would not rise at all as the piston moved outwards, so as a result of transferring energy into the gas the gas will get hotter and it will do work, and in the expression $\Delta U = Q + W$, ΔU will have a positive value because the internal energy increases, Q will have a positive value because energy was transferred *into* the gas through heating and *W* will have a negative value because work has been done *by* the gas as it expanded and moved the piston. This is an **isobaric change**, i.e. a change at constant pressure.

Figure 4.4 shows these different changes on graphs of pressure versus volume. The curves sweeping from high pressure and low volume to low pressure and high volume are isothermals – constant temperature curves.

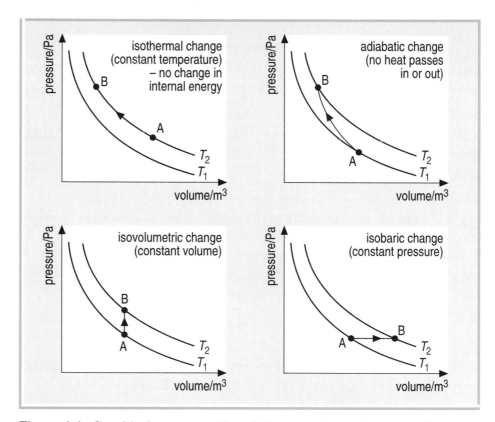

Figure 4.4 Graphical representation of changes in internal energy of a gas

 What type of change is taking place if a gas is heated from outside a sealed rigid container, and what is happening to the gas?

It is an isovolumetric change. The pressure in the gas will rise and its temperature will increase.

Q5 Make a copy of Table 4.3 and fill in the missing cells to summarize all the changes described and the way the first law of thermodynamics accounts for the energy. Two of the rows have been completed for you. ◆

Table 4.3 Summary of internal energy changes

Change	W	Q	ΔU	Equation
adiabatic expansion	+	0	+	$\Delta U = W$
adiabatic compression				
isothermal expansion				
isothermal compression				
isovolumetric heating				
isovolumetric cooling				
isobaric expansion	–	+	+	$\Delta U = Q + W$
isobaric compression				

Now, back to the four-stroke engine.

1   The intake stroke of the engine involves drawing a fixed mass of gas at temperature T_0 from the outside into the cylinder.

If this happened slowly the change would be isobaric, but in practice it happens quickly so it is approximately an adiabatic change in which the work done on the gas, W_1, has a negative value (i.e. the gas does work). So the internal energy of the gas will fall slightly and this will contribute to the inefficiency of the engine.

The temperature of the gas must now quickly rise to the equilibrium temperature of the engine, T_1, so the energy supplied by the heating, Q_1, has a positive value.

2   The compression stroke also happens quickly, so this is an adiabatic change too, but work done on the gas, W_2, has a positive value and the temperature of the gas rises to T_2.

3   The ignition/power stroke is quite complicated thermodynamically. The number of molecules of gas is not constant. The fuel consists of large hydrocarbon molecules and air; after combustion most of the molecules are much simpler (ideally carbon dioxide and water) and there are more of them.

Basically, though, an amount of thermal energy, Q_2 (positive), is supplied to the gas very quickly. The spark ignites the mixture, the temperature rises from T_2 to T_3, and then the gases expand adiabatically and work done on the gas, W_3, has a large negative value (i.e. the gas does work) and the temperature falls to T_4.

The temperature falls quickly back to the equilibrium temperature of the engine, T_1, so the adiabatic expansion is followed by an isovolumetric change. The thermal energy supplied to the gas, Q_3, has a negative value so thermal energy is being transferred out of the gas and the engine.

4   The exhaust stroke is similar to the intake stroke, though the work done on the gas, W_4, is positive. This is unfortunate, since this energy is being transferred to the gas when it is waste and on its way out of the engine, so it contributes to the inefficiency of the engine.

You can see that stages 1, 2 and 4 all involve energy being spent. Only stage 3 involves extracting useful energy from the fuel.

The total amount of energy supplied to the gas $= Q_1 + W_2 + Q_2 + W_4$

The total amount of energy removed from the gas $= W_1 + W_3 + Q_3$

The most significant terms are Q_2, which is most of the energy transferred into the engine through heating, Q_3, which is most of the energy lost to the engine through it cooling (heating its surroundings) and W_3, which is the useful work done by the engine. Ignoring the other terms and equating the energy supplied to the amount of energy removed we get

$$Q_2 = W_3 + Q_3$$

The useful work done is given by

$$W_3 = Q_2 - Q_3$$

So the efficiency, $\varepsilon = \dfrac{W_3}{Q_2}$, can be expressed as

$$\varepsilon \approx \frac{Q_2 - Q_3}{Q_2}$$

The change in the internal energy of a mass of gas, m, is given by

$$\Delta U = mc\Delta T$$

where c is the **specific heat capacity** and ΔT is the temperature change.

 If the specific heat capacity of the gas in a cylinder is $1000\ \mathrm{J\ kg^{-1}\ K^{-1}}$ and its mass is 7.0×10^{-6} kg, how much energy does it gain when its temperature rises by 100°C?

$\Delta U = mc\Delta T$

$\quad = 7.0 \times 10^{-6}\ \mathrm{kg} \times 1000\ \mathrm{J\,kg^{-1}\,K^{-1}} \times 100\ \mathrm{K}$

$\quad = 0.7\ \mathrm{J}$

The terms in the expression for efficiency above are associated with changes in the internal energy of the gas, so

$$\varepsilon \approx \frac{mc(T_3 - T_2) - mc(T_4 - T_1)}{mc(T_3 - T_2)}$$

$$= \frac{T_3 - T_2 - T_4 + T_1}{T_3 - T_2}$$

$$= 1 - \frac{T_4 - T_1}{T_3 - T_2}$$

To maximize efficiency, the ratio $\dfrac{T_4 - T_1}{T_3 - T_2}$ must be as small as possible.

One way of doing this is to make the ratio of maximum cylinder volume to minimum cylinder volume (the **compression ratio**) as large as possible.

Apart from being an approximation, because of the neglected terms, this treatment assumes that all the fuel is involved in the combustion, but the process is so fast, and the gases are swirling around in the cylinder at such high speeds, that this is never the case – which is why the exhaust contains hydrocarbons and carbon monoxide.

Q6 A typical family car in Britain today can travel about 8.00 miles per litre of petrol and has an engine efficiency of about 18%. The output of the engine of this car would be approximately 200 MJ on a journey of 250 miles that takes 5 hours.

(a) List at least three causes of the low efficiency of the car.

(b) What is the average energy output from the engine per mile?

(c) What is the average energy input to the engine per mile?

(d) How much energy is provided by each litre of petrol?

(e) If the engine runs at an average rate of 2000 revolutions per minute and it has four cylinders, how much useful energy is supplied by each power stroke of a cylinder? ◆

4.4 Engine efficiency

The efficiency of a typical car engine is very low (around 20%). The engine is the least efficient component of a car, and the energy losses from it are greater than the losses due to drag.

Q7 (a) A car requires 80.0 MJ of useful energy from its engine to complete a journey of 100 miles. One litre of petrol provides 35.0 MJ of energy to the engine. Calculate the number miles the car can travel per litre of petrol if the engine has an efficiency of 20%

(b) The engine is replaced by one with an efficiency of 30%. Calculate the improved fuel consumption of the car in miles per litre. ◆

The situation would probably be better than the question implies. A more efficient engine means that a car can have a smaller fuel tank and a less sophisticated cooling system to remove waste energy. The engine itself may be lighter and smaller as less heat is being produced. A lighter car is more fuel efficient.

Reducing the fuel consumption of an engine reduces the quantity of emissions. It is also very likely that the increased efficiency has at least partly been achieved by improving the combustion process, thus reducing the products of incomplete ignition such as carbon monoxide, nitrogen oxides and hydrocarbons.

Ways in which engines are being made more efficient will be described in the next section.

4.5   Efficient use of cars

Cars can be driven to maximize their efficiency. If a driver is aware of how to do this not only does the environment suffer less, but the driver pays less to travel the same distance in probably the same time. This is explained in Section 5.

 In what other way can cars be used more efficiently as a means of transport?

People doing the same journey can travel together in one car (car pooling).

When petrol prices are high and/or the supply cannot meet the demand, car pooling becomes popular through necessity. Halving the number of cars on the roads improves the traffic flow and emissions are more than halved.

4.6   Alternative fuels

There are fuels that burn more cleanly than petrol and produce less of the polluting chemicals, these are **biomass** fuels. Over half a million cars in Brazil run on alcohol (ethanol) produced from sugar and other plant material. The exhaust from one of these cars contains just carbon dioxide and water vapour. The plants grown to replace those that have provided the alcohol will resynthesize the carbon dioxide, so the net contribution to the **greenhouse effect** is zero. (You will learn more about the greenhouse effect in Section 6.)

A drawback of these fuels is that large areas of land are required to grow the plants that are the source of the fuel. An alternative is to use methanol produced from natural gas, but this is expensive and there are also other problems associated with it – cold start difficulties and safety (it burns with an invisible flame). It can be used by blending it with petrol (e.g. M85 – 15% methanol and 85% petrol) so that the damaging emissions are at least reduced. Of course, unlike sugar, natural gas is not a sustainable source and the carbon dioxide produced is not resynthesized by the crop that produces the fuel.

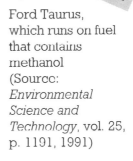

Ford Taurus, which runs on fuel that contains methanol (Source: *Environmental Science and Technology*, vol. 25, p. 1191, 1991)

It has only been economical to produce these fuels when petrol prices have been high and it is most likely that in future they will be used mainly to blend with petrol to produce a cleaner fuel.

Lead-free petrol has become very common in the last few years. An additive consisting of a lead compound was introduced into petrol in the 1930s to improve the performance of the engine (reduce incomplete combustion and so increase the efficiency). Improved engine design and refining processes that can produce higher-grade petrols have made the lead additive unnecessary.

All energy transfer processes, including those that involve heating, are less than 100% efficient – some of the energy will always be wasted. However, an electric car would be far more efficient than a petrol car, and, even taking into account efficiency losses at the power station, electric trains are more efficient than diesel trains. If the electricity has been generated in a traditional power station the pollutants are produced there rather than by the car or train itself, although the amount of pollution will be less. (In Scandinavia, one electric rail line is powered wholly by wind generated electricity.)

 Why would the combustion process in a power station be more efficient than that in a car engine?

The combustion in a power station is continuous, in an car engine the combustion must take place in a very short time and is less likely to be complete.

Solar powered cars are more efficient than petrol driven cars and do not rely upon recharging batteries with electricity generated by power stations that consume fuel and produce pollution. The fact that solar cells are inefficient does not matter from the point of view of the energy wasted (it was all 'free' anyway), but it does mean that solar cars have to be very small and light, and the Sun must be bright! Perhaps, in the future, they will become practical for general use.

A solar car

You can learn more about the efficiency of the electric motor by doing Exploration 5.3 in Section 5.

4.7 Monitoring exhaust emissions

If a car engine is not operating properly, perhaps the timing of the spark from the plug doesn't coincide with the right point in the engine cycle, the engine will be less efficient and will produce poor-quality exhaust. Monitoring the exhaust from motor vehicles, which is a routine part of testing cars now, will identify vehicles that are bad polluters.

Vehicle manufacturers have developed sensors for a variety of exhaust chemicals and engine malfunctions such as misfires, and these have become part of on-board diagnostic systems. The Ford Motor Company has been operating experimental vehicles with on-board diagnostic systems since the early 1990s. They have been capable of monitoring and controlling a variety of engine operating parameters, including real-time emissions. (This means that while the vehicle is actually on the road the operation of the car is adjusted to keep emissions low.) These experiments have been very successful, and close agreement between the measurements of on-board systems and the measurements of larger-scale systems in garages has been achieved.

On-board diagnostic systems will provide drivers with indications of when servicing is required. A memory in the system will store data that can be downloaded so that mechanics can identify intermittent problems and check that legal specifications are always being met by the vehicle.

4.8 Removing emissions from car exhaust

The alternative to using a fuel that does not produce harmful chemical products is to use the conventional fuel but prevent the pollutants from escaping.

Catalytic converters have been installed on virtually every passenger car and light truck in the USA since 1975. A car with a catalytic converter must use lead-free petrol. The exhaust gases pass through a structure with a large surface area that is coated with metals such as platinum, palladium and rhodium. Nitrogen oxides, carbon monoxide and hydrocarbons are prompted to react with each other to produce nitrogen, carbon dioxide and water. The catalytic converter does not, of course, reduce the emission of carbon dioxide, but it reduces the other pollutants by about 90%. Although the number of vehicles in the USA has increased considerably in the last 20 years, the air is generally cleaner now.

There are disadvantages, of course: a car with a catalytic converter is more expensive to buy and less efficient to run. A catalytic converter is designed and engineered to work effectively for at least five years. It is essential that the use of catalytic converters is backed by legislation and monitoring to ensure that the advantages are maintained. In a few years from now, vehicles will be produced with the ability to continuously monitor their own catalyst function so that government monitoring programmes will be less necessary.

4.9 Recycling

Motor vehicles are made from a very wide range of different materials. Some, like the precious metals in catalytic converters, are valuable and worth recycling for economic reasons. But it is important for environmental reasons that all the other materials should be recycled too. This reduces pollution, saves energy and avoids further depleting finite resources.

In countries where labour is cheap, recycling is a way of life for many people; but to make it cost-effective in developed countries it has to be given serious and detailed consideration at the vehicle design stage. Environmental issues are now so important that many motor companies are actively involved in research to develop vehicles that can be almost completely recycled.

Smokey Mountain in Manila – people scrape a living from finding material that can be recycled

Achievements

After working through this section you should be able to:

- analyse data using logarithms to obtain linear plots
- understand and use thermodynamic terminology to describe the operation of an internal combustion engine
- apply the first law of thermodynamics to different problems
- describe several environmental concerns associated with the number of motor vehicles being used and the anticipated growth in this number.

Glossary

Adiabatic change A change in which there is no energy gain or loss by the system undergoing the change. If a gas expands adiabatically its temperature goes down because the work done is obtained from a transformation of internal energy. If it is compressed adiabatically the work done on it is transformed into more internal energy, so the temperature increases.

Biomass Living mass. In our present context it refers to living mass that may be used to produce fuel.

Catalytic converter A device incorporated into the exhaust system of a motor vehicle. Chemical reactions that change harmful chemicals into less harmful ones are encouraged by catalysts. The catalysts themselves remain unchanged and can be recycled when the device is scrapped.

Compression ratio The ratio of the maximum to the minimum engine cylinder volumes. Increasing this ratio increases the efficiency of the engine, but there is a limit to its value; if it is too high, the fuel in the cylinder ignites too early (pre-ignition), which can damage the engine.

First law of thermodynamics An application of the law of conservation of energy. An increase in the internal energy of a system is equal to the sum of the heat put into the system and the work done on the system: $\Delta U = Q + W$.

Greenhouse effect The natural heating of the biosphere due to the absorption of re-emitted infrared radiation by gases, such as carbon dioxide, in the atmosphere.

Internal combustion engine An engine that produces rotational kinetic energy by the combustion of a fuel enclosed in cylinders by pistons connected to a crankshaft. This is the most common means of powering road vehicles and the most common fuel used is petrol. Other flammable gases, such as alcohol vapour and natural gas, can be used.

Isobaric change A change in which the pressure remains constant. If a gas is heated isobarically it must expand to maintain its pressure, and so it does work as its temperature rises. If it is cooled it contracts, and work is done on it by the external pressure.

Isothermal change A change in which the temperature is constant. The energy transferred to a gas by heating is balanced by the work done by the gas, and vice versa, to maintain the temperature, assuming that no chemical changes take place.

Isovolumetric change A change in which the volume remains constant. If a gas neither expands nor is compressed no energy is transferred as work, so any heating or cooling of the system is accounted for by an increase or decrease in the internal energy that is observed as an increase or decrease in the temperature.

Logarithms The logarithm of a number is a unique numerical value that is the power to which a base number must be raised to equal the number. Common logarithms use 10 as the base number, so log (1000) = 3 as 10^3 = 1000. Natural logarithms use e as the base number, so ln (1000) = 6.908 as $e^{6.908}$ = 1000.

Specific heat capacity Unit: joule per kilogram per kelvin (J kg^{-1} K^{-1}). The amount of heat required to raise one unit mass of material by one unit of temperature. It is a property of the material.

Answers to Ready to Study test

R1

(a)

$$s = 5.00\,\text{ms}^{-1} \times 10\,\text{s} + 8.00\,\text{m}$$

$$= 58\,\text{m}$$

(b)

$$s = 5.00\,\text{ms}^{-1} \times 100\,\text{s} + 8.00\,\text{m}$$

$$= 508\,\text{m}$$

R2

(a) 0 m.

(b) 0.3 m.

(c) 21 m.

R3

$$\rho = \frac{m}{V}$$

so

$$V = \frac{m}{\rho}$$

$$= \frac{1.0 \times 10^9\,\text{kg}}{1.0 \times 10^3\,\text{kg}\,\text{m}^{-3}}$$

$$= 1.0 \times 10^6\,\text{m}^3$$

R4

$$P = \frac{F}{A}$$

so

$$A = \frac{F}{P}$$

$$= \frac{250\,\text{kg} \times g}{10 \times 10^3\,\text{Pa}}$$

$$= \frac{250\,\text{kg} \times 9.81\,\text{ms}^{-2}}{10 \times 10^3\,\text{Pa}}$$

$$= 0.25\,\text{m}^2 \text{ (to two significant figures)}$$

R5

Change in gravitational potential energy

$$= mg\Delta h$$

$$= mc\Delta T$$

so

$$g\Delta h = c\Delta T$$

therefore

$$c = \frac{g\Delta h}{\Delta T}$$

$$= \frac{10\,\text{ms}^{-2} \times 30\,\text{m}}{0.1\,\text{K}}$$

$$= 3000\,\text{J}\,\text{kg}^{-1}\,\text{K}^{-1}$$

R6

Absolute zero or 0 K.

R7

(a) Efficiency $= \dfrac{\text{useful energy output}}{\text{total energy input}}$

(If percentages are required, the equation needs to be multiplied by 100.)

(b) The potential energy, E_{pot}, gained by the object is equivalent to the useful energy output in the equation in (a). So

$$E_{pot} = \text{efficiency} \times \text{total energy input}$$

$$= \frac{75}{100} \times 240\,\text{J}$$

$$= 180\,\text{J}$$

Answers to questions in the text

Q1

(a) The gradient is $n = 4$, and constant is $k = 10$.

(b) $y = 10x^4$

(c) The predicted number of motor vehicles in the world by the year 2000 is 100 million and by 2050 it is 5062 million.

Q2

Mass of exhaust = volume × density

$$= 1.00 \times 10^{13}\,\text{m}^3 \times 1.30\,\text{kg}\,\text{m}^{-3}$$

$$= 1.30 \times 10^{13}\,\text{kg}$$

$$\text{Volume of layer} = \frac{\text{mass}}{\text{density}}$$

$$= \text{thickness} \times 4\pi r^2$$

So

$$\text{thickness} = \frac{\text{mass}}{\text{density} \times 4\pi r^2}$$

$$= \frac{1.30 \times 10^{13}\,\text{m}^3}{1000\,\text{kg}\,\text{m}^{-3} \times 4\pi \left(6.40 \times 10^6\,\text{m}\right)^2}$$

$$= 0.025\,\text{mm}$$

(to three significant figures)

Q3

$$\text{Petrol used per revolution} = \frac{9.0 \times 10^{-3}\,\text{m}^3}{60\,\text{min} \times 2000\,\text{min}^{-1}}$$

$$= 7.5 \times 10^{-8}\,\text{m}^3$$

Q4

See Figure 4.5. Crankpins connect the pistons to the crankshaft, which rotates. These pivot at both ends. The vertical motion of the pistons is converted into the rotary motion of the crankshaft. The diagram is very simplified.

Q5

Change	W	Q	ΔU	Equation
adiabatic expansion	+	0	+	$\Delta U = W$
adiabatic compression	−	0	−	$\Delta U = W$
isothermal expansion	+	−	0	$W + Q = 0$
isothermal compression	−	+	0	$W + Q = 0$
isovolumetric heating	0	+	+	$\Delta U = Q$
isovolumetric cooling	0	−	−	$\Delta U = Q$
isobaric expansion	−	+	+	$\Delta U = Q + W$
isobaric compression	+	−	−	$\Delta U = Q + W$

Q6

(a) Air drag, friction in the engine and other moving parts of the car, friction between the tyres and the road, heat losses from the engine.

(b)

$$\frac{200 \times 10^6\,\text{J}}{250\,\text{mile}} = 8.00 \times 10^5\,\text{J}\,\text{mile}^{-1}$$

(c)

$$\frac{8.00 \times 10^5\,\text{J}\,\text{mile}^{-1} \times 100}{18} = 4.44 \times 10^6\,\text{J}\,\text{mile}^{-1}$$

(to three significant figures)

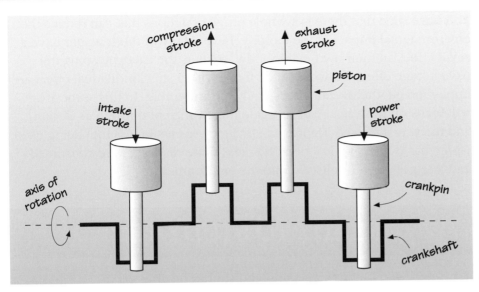

Figure 4.5
Answer to Question 4

(d)

4.44×10^6 J mile^{-1} $\times 8.00$ mile litre^{-1}

$$= 3.55 \times 10^7 \text{ J litre}^{-1}$$

(to three significant figures)

(e)

Number of power strokes per mile

$$= 4 \times 2000 \text{ power strokes min}^{-1}$$

$$\times \frac{5 \times 60 \text{ min}}{250 \text{ mile}}$$

$$= 9600 \text{ power strokes per mile}$$

Q7

(a)

Useful energy from 1 litre $= 35.0$ MJ litre$^{-1} \times \dfrac{20}{100}$

$$= 7.00 \text{ MJ litre}^{-1}$$

Useful energy per mile $= \dfrac{80.0 \text{ MJ}}{100 \text{ mile}}$

$$= 0.800 \text{ MJ mile}^{-1}$$

Number of miles per litre $= \dfrac{7.00 \text{ MJ litre}^{-1}}{0.800 \text{ MJ mile}^{-1}}$

$$= 8.75 \text{ mile litre}^{-1}$$

(b)

Useful energy per litre $= 7.00$ MJ litre$^{-1} \times \dfrac{30\%}{20\%}$

$$= 10.5 \text{ MJ litre}^{-1}$$

Number of miles per litre $= \dfrac{10.5 \text{ MJ litre}^{-1}}{0.800 \text{ MJ mile}^{-1}}$

$$= 13.1 \text{ mile litre}^{-1}$$

(to three significant figures)

83

You have seen that there is a whole range of actions that can reduce the environmental impact of the motor vehicle. Many of them would have a small effect on their own, while a few, such as the catalytic converter, have a huge effect. However, if all those with a small individual effect are implemented, the overall effect can be considerable. In this section we will focus on how a car can be made more efficient through its design and the way it is used. Improved efficiency results in less fuel being used, which has two ecological benefits – less finite resources are consumed and less pollution is released into the environment.

READY TO STUDY TEST

Before you begin this section you should be able to:

- recall and use the relationship
  work = force × distance moved by force
- apply the law of conservation of energy
- explain the part played by friction in limiting the efficiency of machines
- recall and use expressions for kinetic energy and gravitational potential energy
- calculate the power output of an electric heater, given the voltage and current supplied
- calculate total energy supplied, given the power and time
- describe the operation of a simple electrical potential divider circuit.

QUESTIONS

R1 The average force exerted by the power system of a car is 1000 N. The car has accelerated from rest to a speed of 10 m s^{-1} and travelled a distance of 100 m while this force has been applied. It has a mass of 1000 kg. Calculate: (a) the work done by the power system, (b) the final kinetic energy of the car, (c) the efficiency of the whole system.

R2 A 10.0 kg mass is released from rest 5.0 m above the ground. If air drag is neglected, how much kinetic energy does it have just before it hits the ground and how fast is it travelling? (Use $g = 9.81$ N kg^{-1})

R3 An electric lamp is rated as 60 W and is operated from a 240 V supply. (a) What electric current will flow through it? (b) How long will it take to use 4.8×10^4 J of energy?

R4 Two resistors, one having a resistance of 10 Ω and the other 40 Ω, are connected in series between the terminals of a 15 V battery. What is the total current that flows from the battery and what is the potential difference across each of the resistors?

5.1 Efficiency

A number of things affect the efficiency of a vehicle; we will take a look at the following:

■ body structure and shape

■ driving technique

■ engine design.

Body structure and shape

Where does all the energy provided by a car engine go? A car starts from rest, accelerates to its cruising speed, travels some distance and then slows down and comes to rest again. The car has no kinetic energy at the start of its journey and none at the end, fuel has been used up, but all the energy has been transferred. Consider the three parts of the journey:

■ *Acceleration* The car's kinetic energy increases, some of the energy supplied by the engine is transferred because of **friction** and air **drag**.

■ *Constant speed* The car transfers energy because of friction and air drag, but this is balanced by a constant supply of energy from the engine.

■ *Slowing down* The engine is allowed to slow down by reducing its supply of fuel so that the energy transfers are not balanced by the supply. The brakes are applied to increase the friction and kinetic energy is transferred to other forms until it is zero again.

The kinetic energy of the car is given by:

$$E_k = \frac{1}{2}mv^2$$

where m is the mass of the car in kilograms, v is the speed of the car in metres per second and E_k is kinetic energy in joules.

There is friction in the engine itself, in the transmission, and there is also **rolling friction**, which accounts for tyres getting warm on a journey – energy is used to compress the part of the tyre coming into contact with the road, but some of this is lost as that part expands again. Rolling friction can account for a large proportion of the energy needed to keep a car moving.

The energy used to compensate for rolling friction is:

$$E_R = C_R\,mgd$$

where C_R is the coefficient of rolling friction, mg is the weight of the car in newtons and d is the length of the journey in metres.

C_R depends upon the type of tyre used and its condition – it would be lowest for worn, over-inflated, radial tyres (and nearly zero for smooth steel wheels like those of a train). Typically it is 0.01–0.02.

The car has to cut its way through the air in front of it, the more streamlined the car, the easier this is. A more detailed consideration of this can be found in the SLIPP unit *Physics on the Move*, which also contains explorations on this topic. The energy lost by a vehicle because of air drag is

$$E_D = \frac{1}{2}C_D\rho v^2 Ad$$

where C_D is the drag coefficient of the vehicle (this is about 0.34 for modern cars), ρ is the density of the air in kg m^{-3}, A is the effective area of the car in m^2 that is presented normally to the air flow.

1
HOUR

Exploration 5.1   The relationship between a car's energy consumption and its speed

About 80% of a car's 'energy bill' is for kinetic energy, rolling friction and air drag, if it hasn't got air-conditioning, power steering and other accessories requiring a lot of energy. This is called the transmission efficiency. In this exploration you will calculate the energy used to drive a 'standard car' on a 'standard journey'.

Standard car

Mass, m = 1000 kg

Area, A = 2.000 m^2

C_R = 0.015

C_D = 0.340

Transmission efficiency = 80%

Standard journey

100 km on flat roads through still air with a density of 1.2 kg m^{-3} at constant speed apart from brief initial acceleration and final slowing down. The journey is to take less than 5 hours. (Use g = 9.81 m s^{-2}.)

Calculate the 'energy bill' for the car doing the journey at a range of different speeds and record the data obtained in a table.

Plot the data in a graph of energy consumed versus speed.

Draw some conclusions from the data – for example, how is the energy bill affected by speed? Is it a good idea to turn off the engine while waiting at traffic lights?

Exploration 5.2   The effects of mass, rolling friction and air drag on a car's energy consumption

1 HOUR

In this exploration you will modify the specifications of the 'standard car' in the last exploration to find the energy bill for a different standard journey.

Standard car A

Mass, m = 500 kg

Area, A = 2.000 m^2

C_R = 0.015

C_D = 0.30

Standard car B

Mass, m = 1000 kg

Area, A = 2.000 m^2

C_R = 0.015

C_D = 0.30

Standard car C

Mass, m = 2000 kg

Area, A = 2.000 m^2

C_R = 0.015

C_D = 0.30

Standard car D

Mass, m = 1000 kg

Area, A = 2.000 m^2

C_R = 0.010

C_D = 0.30

Standard car E

Mass, m = 1000 kg

Area, A = 2.000 m^2

C_R = 0.020

C_D = 0.30

Standard car F

Mass, m = 1000 kg

Area, A = 1.000 m^2

C_R = 0.015

C_D = 0.30

Standard car G

Mass, m = 1000 kg

Area, A = 3.000 m^2

C_R = 0.015

C_D = 0.30

Standard car H

Mass, m = 1000 kg

Area, A = 2.000 m^2

C_R = 0.015

C_D = 0.20

Standard car I

Mass, m = 1000 kg

Area, A = 2.000 m^2

C_R = 0.015

C_D = 0.40

Transmission efficiencies are all 80%.

Standard journey

100 km on flat roads through still air with a density of 1.2 kg m^{-3} at constant speed of 100 km h^{-1}, apart from brief initial acceleration and final slowing down. (Use g = 9.81 m s^{-2}.)

Calculate the energy bill of each of the standard cars A to I.

Record the results of the various changes graphically.

Draw conclusions, backed by numerical evidence, about the relative effectiveness of each of the changes.

The values of these quantities for real cars are often arrived at through compromises. The shape of a car needs to be attractive (fashion is probably as important to the motorist as aerodynamics) and the car has to be functional – a family car must have space for a family and its luggage, and it must be comfortable on long journeys. Also, safety is more important than energy efficiency: the driver must have good visibility and the car must have good road holding in a variety of conditions – who would want to take off every time the car goes over the top of a hill in a head-wind? Tyres, too, are designed for safety – minimizing rolling friction would result in a very unsafe tyre.

Vehicle manufacturers are exploring ways of producing lightweight body structures. New materials could result in improved fuel economy, safety and reliability. Aluminium cannot be stamped into shape like sheet steel, so the research is investigating alloys, heat treatments and **super-plastic forming** as means of shaping aluminium into body panels. They are also developing design and manufacturing methods to make use of polymer composites to replace at least some car components that have traditionally been made of metal.

Driving technique

The way a person drives a car can effect the fuel economy, although often matters are beyond the driver's control – roads become congested or driving conditions are very variable.

You have already seen (in Section 4) that work needs to be done to draw fuel into the cylinder of the engine and also to push the exhaust gases out after the power stroke. The accelerator pedal controls the throttle, which controls the flow of fuel into the engine; the more nearly closed it is, the more it restricts the flow of fuel and air into the cylinder. Driving slowly involves keeping the throttle nearer to being closed – maximizing the work that has to be done to get fuel into the cylinders.

If the most common speed of cars is, say, 50 mph, then to maximize efficiency car throttles should be fully open at this speed. However, that would mean that cars would have less and less acceleration as they approached that speed, which would not be practical. So the throttle isn't fully open for most cars until they are travelling at more than 70 mph, which means that below this speed cars do not have maximum efficiency as far as fuel pumping is concerned.

In Section 4.2 you saw that, because of air drag, the slower a car travels the more fuel efficient it is. Now we have a phenomenon that implies the reverse – the more open the throttle, i.e. the faster the car is going, the more efficient it will be.

The combined effect of these two opposing phenomena is a situation in which there is an optimum speed for fuel economy (see Figure 5.1). This may be as low as 30 mph for some cars; this results in cars generally running at less than maximum efficiency if the most common speed is 50 mph. If the 'throttle fully open at 50 mph' situation were adopted, then efficiency at all speeds below 50 mph would increase by perhaps 3%.

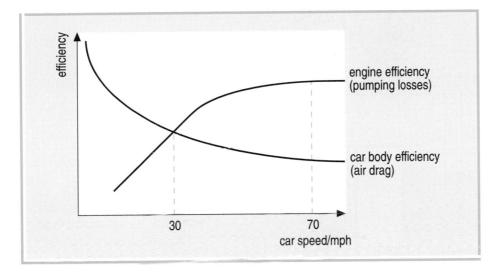

Figure 5.1
Effects of pumping losses and air drag on efficiency

 Why would the 'throttle fully open at 50 mph' situation increase the efficiency at all speeds below 50 mph.

The curve in Figure 5.1 corresponding to the effect of pumping losses would be shifted to the left, i.e. the plateau would move so that it occurred at 50 mph. The combined effect (the overall efficiency of the car) is related to the products of the values of the two efficiencies illustrated in the figure, so it would have a higher value at all speeds up to the maximum 'flat-road, still-air' speed of the car, which is 50 mph.

 Exploration 5.3 Does the efficiency of an electric motor system depend on the speed of the motor?

1 HOUR

Apparatus:
◆ electric motor (e.g. a Technical Lego motor) ◆ pulley on a shaft (e.g. an assembly using Lego) ◆ low-voltage d.c. power supply (9 V) ◆ rheostat to use as the potential divider (potentiometer) ◆ ammeter ◆ voltmeter ◆ string ◆ drive belt ◆ hanging mass (e.g. 100 g) ◆ G-clamp

Set up the motor/pulley/string/mass system shown in Figure 5.2 overleaf so that the mass is raised by winding the string on to the shaft of the large pulley. Connect the motor to the inset circuit. Be careful not to supply too large a potential difference to the motor. If in doubt, get the circuit checked before you switch it on. Don't strain the motor by using a heavy load. Start with a low potential difference and a small load, you can increase them later.

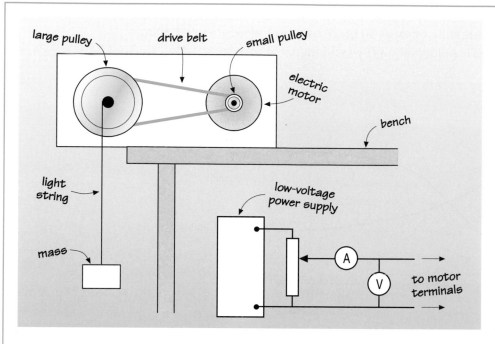

Figure 5.2
Measuring the efficiency of an electric motor system

The **potentiometer** can be used to vary the speed at which the motor raises the mass hanging from the string.

The energy supplied to the motor is given by $E_{in} = VIt$, where V is the voltage in volts and I is the current in amps supplied by the power supply, and t is the time in seconds taken to raise the mass.

The work done by the motor in raising the mass is given by $E_{out} = mgh$, where m is the mass in kilograms, g is the acceleration due to gravity (9.81 m s^{-2}) and h is the height through which the mass is raised in metres.

The efficiency of the system is E_{out}/E_{in}.

The average speed in m s^{-1} at which the mass is raised is given by $v = h/t$, which can be taken as a measure of the speed of the motor.

Use the system to raise a fixed mass through a fixed distance at a range of different speeds. Repeat your readings several times for each different setting of the potentiometer.

Tabulate all the data and determine the average values of E_{in}, E_{out} and v for each setting of the potentiometer. Plot a graph of efficiency versus speed as you collect the data so that you can identify suspect data and can look for trends. (*Note:* The earliest data you collect should be for the maximum voltage of the motor and the minimum that will raise the mass, you can then establish the range of values for the graph.)

Does there appear to be an optimum motor speed for efficient operation of the system?

Attempt to explain the maximum efficiency operating conditions of the lifting system.

Driving conditions can seriously affect the overall efficiency of car transport. In a traffic jam cars continue to use petrol and produce exhaust without actually moving. All the energy is wasted.

 Why do driving conditions involving frequent changes in speed (e.g. when travelling on a road with many tight bends) contribute to the inefficiency of car transport?

Fuel is used to give a car kinetic energy to travel at a certain speed, any reduction in speed due to driving conditions amounts to energy lost through friction, drag, etc., which has to be provided again by the engine when the car's speed increases again.

Ideally, cars should be able to travel at a constant speed that optimizes the efficiency of the car. Roads need to have sufficient capacity for the car flow so that congestion does not occur and cars are sufficiently spaced to avoid frequent acceleration and braking. Several lanes allow different vehicles to travel at different speeds to optimize their efficiency and to allow overtaking. This is the idea behind motorways; unfortunately, the majority of drivers increase their speed on motorways so that their cars are running very inefficiently because of the increase in air drag. Doubling a car's speed quadruples the air drag on it because the drag depends upon the speed squared. Lower speed limits would increase the efficiency of car transport significantly and be popular with pedestrians and cyclists, but they would not be popular with most car users.

Engine design

The efficiency of a petrol engine is increased by increasing the compression ratio. However, if the compression ratio is made very high, the temperature of the fuel/air mixture rises so much, because of its adiabatic compression, that it ignites before the spark is produced by the sparkplug. This is called pre-ignition and it tends to push the piston down while it is still on its up stroke. This produces a vibration called knocking, but more importantly the engine can be seriously damaged.

Diesel engines

The diesel engine avoids pre-ignition because only air is admitted to the cylinder during the intake stroke, the fuel is injected after the compression stroke in atomized form. The air already in the cylinder is at a high temperature so the fuel ignites to produce the power stroke without the need of a spark.

Diesel engines have better fuel economy and they do not need an ignition control system, which means they are longer lasting and should need less maintenance. But the exhaust contains large amounts of carbon particles and nitrogen oxides.

Lean-burn engines

The fuel/air mixture in the diesel engine is 'lean' in that, overall, it contains more air than a normal petrol engine. However, the mixture is fuel rich at the points of ignition. If a self-sustaining flame could be achieved in a lean mixture the engine would be more efficient and the exhaust would contain fewer products of incomplete combustion, such as carbon, carbon monoxide, hydrocarbons and nitrogen oxides, because of the higher concentration of oxygen in the cylinder.

Ford produced a spark-ignited lean-burn engine in the 1970s (the PROCO), but it did not meet emission standards and there were driving problems. Producing a satisfactory lean-burn engine is well worth the effort, however. The efficiency is given by:

$$\varepsilon = 1 - \frac{1}{r^{\gamma - 1}}$$

where r is the compression ratio (maximum/minimum cylinder volume) and γ is the ratio of the specific heat capacity at constant pressure, c_P, to the specific heat capacity at constant volume, c_V, of the fuel/air mixture.

 c_P/c_V is always greater than 1 – why?

The specific heat capacity of a gas is the amount of thermal energy required to raise the temperature of unit mass of the gas by 1 K. If the gas is heated at constant pressure it expands and so does work. When it is heated at constant volume it does not expand and it does not do work, so the amount of heat energy required for the same temperature rise is less.

If $c_P > c_V$ then $c_P/c_V > 1$. $\gamma = 1.40$ for pure air, but $\gamma = 1.30$ for the lean limit of a typical modern engine. The value $\gamma = 1.40$ is approached asymptotically as the fuel/air mixture is diluted with more air.

Q1 What is the improvement in the efficiency of an engine with a compression ratio of 10 if the value of γ is changed from 1.30 to 1.35 by using a leaner fuel/air mixture? ◆

The problems with lean-burn engines stem from one factor – the flame propagates more slowly through the combustion chamber. This means that the combustion does not take place at nearly constant volume so some work is lost, misfires are more likely and incomplete combustion can occur.

Honda, Mitsubishi and Toyota are all producing vehicles with lean-burn engines, but none of them satisfy the strict Californian standards for emission of nitrogen oxides. Current catalytic converter efficiency is not high enough to remove the extra quantities of nitrogen oxides that lean-burn engines produce. There are also driving problems – there is a delay when extra power is demanded from the engine.

Vehicle manufacturers (including Ford, Honda, Mitsubishi and Toyota) are actively involved in the race to produce a lean-burn engine without any of the pollution or driveability problems. The ability to switch to lean-burn for cruising speed only and computer control systems linked to in-cylinder pressure sensors are among the solutions being considered. Improving the efficiency of catalytic converters is also a high priority.

Hybrid vehicles

In 1979, Ford's research laboratory produced a van with a 17 kW electric motor in parallel with a standard petrol engine. It had a very limited electric range, but it wasn't intended to function as an electric vehicle – the petrol engine would normally run all the time. The advantage of a hybrid vehicle is that the petrol engine can run at a constant rate, and this rate can be optimized for efficiency and clean emissions. When the petrol engine is supplying more energy than required for driving, the extra can be converted into electricity and stored in batteries. When more power is required than the steady level delivered by the petrol engine, the electric system provides it by using the previously stored energy.

Ford also produced the Aachen vehicle in a project with Aachen University, which was shown at the Frankfurt Auto Show in 1993. It also has an electric-only range capability.

Research into hybrid vehicles is ongoing – Ford is aiming to produce a vehicle that achieves three times the fuel efficiency of today's vehicles. Although the demonstration hybrid vehicles achieved impressive improvements in fuel economy, the cost of the extra components (particularly for energy storage) is a major drawback as it runs into thousands of pounds. Alternative energy stores (flywheels running on magnetic bearings in a vacuum, ultracapacitors, bipolar batteries) and simpler engines (turbine engines) are being looked at as ways of reducing the total cost of a hybrid vehicle.

The Aachen vehicle (Source: *Ford Highlights*, vol. 3, no. 4, p. 3, Figure 3)

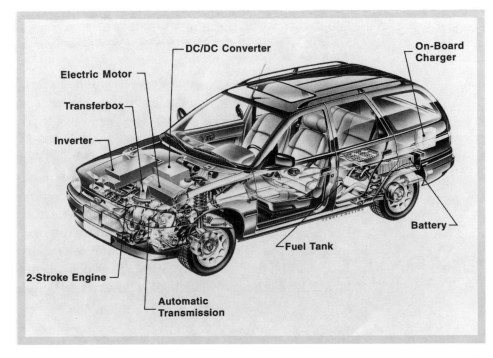

Electric vehicles

In 1995, Peugeot made the 106 Electric available for the general market as a quiet and economical car for urban use. Its nickel–cadmium batteries can be fully charged from the domestic mains supply (or from a public outlet in a garage) in about 8 hours. A full charge can run the car for 90 km at 90 km h^{-1} or 150 km at 50 km h^{-1}. The batteries themselves are rented and are recycled when they wear out. The electric car uses no energy at all when it is stationary, e.g. at traffic lights, and the motor acts as a generator when the car is slowing down. This feature, the limited acceleration and range make electric vehicles ideal for busy city traffic and everyone benefits by having cleaner air.

Peugeot 106

Fuel cells

In a fuel cell, hydrogen and oxygen combine to produce water and electrons, thus generating d.c. electricity. Unlike a battery, the chemicals for the fuel cell must be supplied from an outside source. Theoretically, they can convert fuel to electricity with nearly 100% efficiency. The first hydrogen–oxygen cell was described in 1839; it consisted of two platinum strips immersed in acid – the upper part of one was exposed to hydrogen and the other to oxygen. The most common fuel cells have used potassium hydroxide (an alkali) as the electrolyte. There has also been research on fuel cell systems based on the oxidation of hydrocarbons. These systems can produce electricity from almost any hydrocarbon fuel, including petrol. They produce little pollution and have a high efficiency. Figure 5.3 shows a fuel cell subsystem.

Fuel cells are at present used chiefly in space vehicles, but they have been demonstrated in buses and light trucks in North America and Europe. Fuel cell powered personal vehicles are probably still several decades off.

Friction and lubrication

Overcoming friction in the engine and the transmission of a vehicle accounts for a significant proportion of the useful energy output of the engine. The amount of friction depends upon the lubrication provided and the state of the solid surfaces involved. Lubricants and coatings are the subjects of vast amounts of research by universities, motor vehicle manufacturers and associated industries. Hard coatings based on diamond, glass and carbon, and petrol additives that reduce engine friction are being developed.

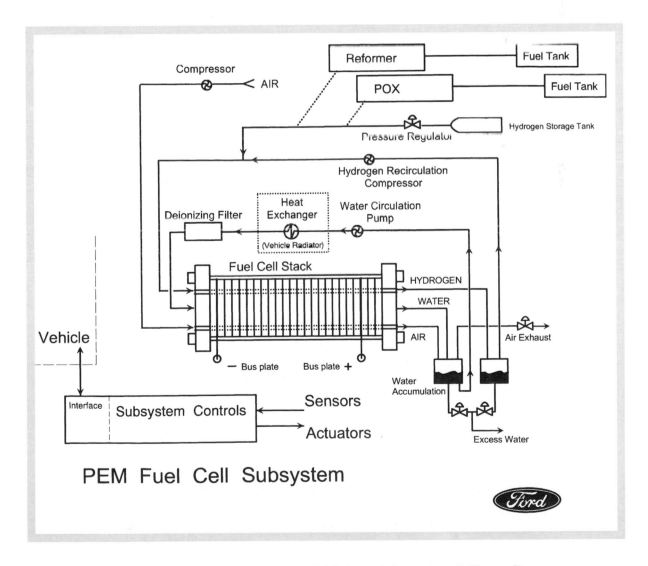

Figure 5.3 Fuel cell subsystem (Source: *Ford Highlights*, vol. 3, no. 4, p. 5, Figure 8)

Exploration 5.4   Investigating friction and lubrication

Apparatus:
- ◆ flat glass plate ◆ several sledges of the same material but different areas
- ◆ range of newtonmeters ◆ range of masses that can be stacked on top of the sledges
- ◆ range of lubricants (e.g. a light oil and a heavy oil)

Using this equipment you can investigate how the frictional force between the sledge and the plate depends on a number of different factors (the contact area, the force pressing the surfaces together and the type of lubricant between the surfaces). You should measure the **static frictional force** (which is equal to the minimum force you need to apply to start relative motion between the sledge and the plate) and the **dynamic frictional force** (which is equal to the force you apply to maintain uniform relative motion). (You will find further information on static and dynamic frictional forces in Section 6.2 of the SLIPP unit *Physics on the Move*.)

Part (i)

Choose a sledge and some masses. Measure the mass of the sledge. Set up the equipment as in Figure 5.4. Don't place any lubricant between the sledge and the plate. Pull on the sledge with the newtonmeter. Measure the static and dynamic frictional forces and repeat your measurements several times to obtain average values.

Place the data in a table with four columns (label these 'Mass/kg', 'Normal force/N', 'Static frictional force/N' and 'Dynamic frictional force/N'. The normal force is equal to the weight of the masses and sledge (total mass $\times g$).

Repeat this with a range of different masses and plot the data as a graph of frictional force versus normal force to obtain two lines on the same axes.

Part (ii)

Measure the masses of all the sledges and determine the areas of their lower surfaces. Choose a mass to place on each sledge in turn that is large enough to make the masses of the sledges negligible.

For each sledge, measure the two frictional forces and record the data in a table. Plot graphs of frictional force against area on the same axes.

Part (iii)

Place some of one of your lubricants on the glass plate and repeat Part (i). Do this for each of your lubricants.

Using the graphs of your data from these experiments, draw conclusions about the dependence of frictional forces on the force pressing two surfaces together, the area of the surfaces in contact and the effect of lubrication.

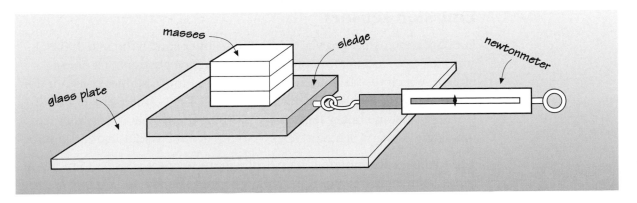

Figure 5.4 Investigating friction and lubrication

Q2 A wooden block, 5 cm × 4 cm × 3 cm has a mass of 0.04 kg. It is on a flat surface with its 3 cm side vertical. The minimum force that causes the block to slide on the surface is 0.18 N.

(a) What is the minimum force required to move the block if its 5 cm side is vertical and you assume all faces of the block are equally smooth?

(b) What is this force if the 4 cm side is vertical and a mass of 0.09 kg has been placed on top of the block? ◆

5.2 Emission control and waste management

Personal vehicles that are able to take us from place to place at reasonably high speeds and can carry a reasonable load (a few friends, luggage, the dog, shopping, etc.) are very much part of modern society in developed countries. The sheer number of these vehicles is sufficient to threaten the environment. It is unrealistic to expect any sudden reduction in the number or a rapid change to an alternative design should a clean one be found. Consequently, authorities like the legislatures in California are encouraging the automobile industry to develop means of minimizing the environmental impact.

There are two distinct aspects to environmental damage caused by motor vehicles. The first, pollution from exhaust gases, has already been considered in earlier sections. In this section we will look at catalytic converters, which remove pollutants from the exhaust, in more detail. The second aspect is the waste produced when a vehicle is scrapped. There are two parts to the solution of this problem – extending the life of motor vehicles and recycling the materials from which they are made. In this section you will discover what the motor vehicle industry is doing about this problem.

Emission sensors

Fuel injection came into wide use in passenger cars in the mid-1980s. It supplies a precise mixture of fuel and air to the cylinders of a petrol engine, which results in cleaner exhaust and improved fuel consumption. The technology has been available since the 1950s, but it was not until stricter emission-control legislation was introduced that it was built into most new cars as a standard feature to replace the traditional carburettor.

The fuel injection system for a petrol engine requires sensors to monitor the oxygen in the exhaust; this shows how efficiently and cleanly the fuel is being burned. The sensor signal is fed into a small computer together with information about engine speed, temperature, etc. Petrol is sent under pressure by a fuel pump into the fuel injection valve, which sprays the fuel into the cylinder where it mixes with incoming air. The computer operates the valve and controls the time that it remains open. The fuel injection computer can compensate for cold starts, high engine temperature, low oxygen concentration at high altitude, and so on, by adjusting the time for which the valve is kept open.

Research is also being done on sensors that can measure the concentrations of other chemicals in the exhaust, such as carbon monoxide, hydrocarbons, nitrogen oxides and sulphur dioxide. Some of the sensors are made from **semiconducting materials** – mainly zirconia, but titanium has also been used. The semiconductor used in an oxygen sensor, for example, has an **electrical conductivity** that is strongly dependent on the concentration of oxygen. So the sensor's resistance depends on the oxygen concentration (electrical conductivity is the reciprocal of **resistivity**). This is very much like the way that a thermistor's resistance depends on temperature or a light-dependent resistor's resistance depends on light level.

Figure 5.5
Getting an oxygen-concentration-dependent voltage from a potential divider incorporating an oxygen sensor

Q3 The resistance, $R\,(\Omega)$, of a TiO_2 oxygen sensor depends upon oxygen concentration, $C\,(\%)$, according to the relationship:

$$\log R = 10 + 0.5 \log C$$

Calculate the resistance of the oxygen sensor when the oxygen concentration is: (a) $1.0 \times 10^{-8}\%$, (b) $5.0 \times 10^{-18}\%$. ◆

Q4 The oxygen sensor described in Question 3 is connected as part of a potential divider, as shown in Figure 5.5

Calculate the output voltage from the potential divider for the two concentrations of oxygen used in Question 3. ◆

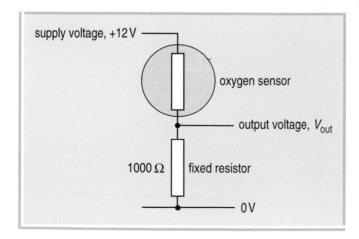

Apparatus:

- light-dependent resistor ◆ selection of fixed resistors ◆ 12 V d.c. power supply
- voltmeter (0–12 V or 0–10 V) ◆ black ink ◆ 500 cm^3 measuring cylinder
- dropper ◆ lamp ◆ clean water

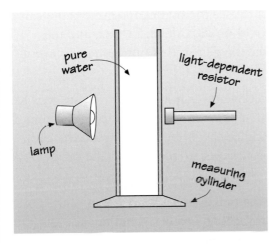

Set up the apparatus and circuit as shown in Figures 5.6 and 5.7. Choose a fixed value resistor so that the output from the circuit is approximately 10 V. Avoid getting the electrical equipment near the water in the measuring cylinder.

Figure 5.6 Arrangement of apparatus to calibrate a light sensor in terms of ink concentration

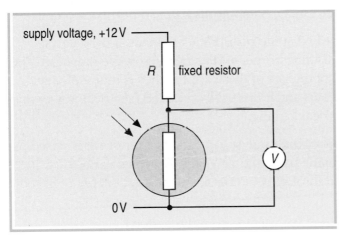

Figure 5.7 The circuit for the light sensor

Draw a table with two columns: ink concentration/drops per litre, and light sensor output/V.

Record the output voltage for 500 cm^3 pure water. Add black ink, one drop at a time, stirring the mixture thoroughly, and record the output voltage after each drop.

Plot the calibration curve of output voltage against ink concentration.

Finally, ask someone to make up a mixture without telling you the concentration. How accurately can you determine the concentration using your apparatus?

Catalytic converters

A catalyst is something that encourages a chemical reaction between other substances without being used up itself. Catalytic converters contain catalysts that promote chemical reactions such as oxidation and reduction. They can reduce the emissions of hydrocarbons, carbon monoxide and nitrogen oxides by more than 90%.

When exhaust gases pass through the converter when it is hot, there is a flow of extra air and the catalyst causes the hydrocarbons and the carbon monoxide to be converted into carbon dioxide and water, and the nitrogen to be separated from the oxygen so that nitrogen gas, carbon dioxide and water are produced.

It is important that the catalytic converter is hot. If the exhaust gases heat up the converter from cold it can take over a minute before it is at its correct operating temperature (called the 'light-off' temperature) and several minutes more until the emissions are reduced to the proper level, see Figure 5.8.

Q5 Use Figure 5.8 to estimate the percentage contribution of the cold start to the total amount of hydrocarbons produced in the exhaust during a one hour journey. You can assume that the average rate of production of hydrocarbons after exactly 3 minutes is 0.025 in normalized units. ◆

Research has also looked at the possibilities of heating the catalyst electrically, with a gasoline burner and using microwave radiation. The potential advantage of the last of these approaches is more efficient heating of the substrates and a drastically reduced electrical power drain compared with electrical heating.

Q6 The temperature of the catalyst in a catalytic converter is raised prior to starting the car engine using the 12 V supply from a car battery. Its temperature is raised through 375°C in 20 s. The total energy required was 7.5×10^4 J.

(a) What electric current was drawn from the battery?

(b) Assuming that the heating process was 1.0% efficient, what is the value of the heat capacity of the catalyst (heat capacity = mass of catalyst × specific heat capacity, $C = mc$).

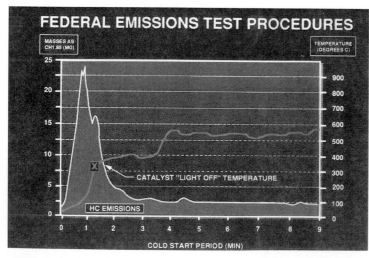

Figure 5.8
Catalyst temperature and hydrocarbon emissions after a cold start (Source: Ford Motor Company)

(c) The catalyst has to be raised through a further 200°C after the engine is started. If the overall effect of the flow of exhaust is to make the heating process 0.25% efficient, how long does it take to achieve this temperature rise?

(d) Initial research results suggest that 50 W of microwave power can achieve the necessary pre-start heating. What is the efficiency of this heating process? ◆

Recycling

In 1990, BMW announced that it was building a car recycling plant. BMW and other car manufacturers are researching the use of alternative materials that can be recycled. This involves assessing several factors in terms of their environmental and economic impacts compared with continuing to use the same materials. These factors are:

- the suitability of the new materials
- the volume of the waste produced during the manufacture of the car and when it is scrapped
- the energy needed for producing the new materials
- the additional costs incurred by changing to the new materials.

Scrapped vehicles are generally dismantled for spare parts. Radiators, catalytic converters, fluids and batteries are normally recycled. After shredding, ferrous metals can be removed magnetically and non-ferrous metals can be sorted out by density. Automobile recycling recovers more than 10 million tonnes of steel and nearly 1 million tonnes of non-ferrous metals in the USA every year. The material from car shredders that cannot be recycled includes plastics, glass and rubber, and it amounts to about 24% of the weight of the original scrap. This is used for landfill, which, in Europe at least, is an expensive means of disposal. In other words, it is now becoming worthwhile economically to increase the proportion of a motor vehicle that can be readily recycled. This is good news for the environment.

Ford, together with Syntene (a thermoplastic rubber supplier), have patented a process to recycle old automobile tyres – 240 million are scrapped worldwide every year. Ford use some products of this recycling process in the manufacture of their own new body parts, such as pedal pads, carpet backing and weather seals.

Gradually, the prospect of a totally recyclable vehicle is getting closer. However, even when this is achieved there will still be an environmental cost. Energy is used to produce every new vehicle and to scrap every old one, and this energy can never be recovered. So it would do the environment a big favour if the useful life of every motor vehicle could be extended.

Extending the useful life of cars

Most people would like a nice, new, shiny car; unfortunately, most of us can't afford it – we have to make do with someone else's cast-off. When someone has just passed their driving test the first thing they want is a car of their own, and the chances are it will have had several previous owners. The problem with a very old car is that maintenance costs can be high. Extending the life of a car doesn't mean we all have to drive the same car for a long time. Probably everyone will keep their car a bit longer before they exchange it and they will all benefit to some extent from lower maintenance costs.

Manufacturers are now working towards a target of at least 100 000 miles for the normal lifetime of a passenger car, which potentially could include most of its parts.

5.3 Computer modelling and simulation

Information technology is now widely used by manufacturers of automobiles. Computers can reduce the cost of designing new components and vehicles by reducing the number of prototypes that have to be produced and giving designers the opportunity to try a wider variety of alternative solutions in the same time. Models and simulations also increase reliability. Computer models have been very successful in helping to improve the fuel economy of vehicles.

Research laboratories are using computers to check the feasibility of manufacturing new shapes and specifications in the sheet metal used for car bodies, and to simulate the performance of transmission systems and engine control systems. They are working towards an easy-to-use complete engine modelling system.

Driving simulators enable engineers to study how human beings interact with the various systems built into cars to improve their performance and safety, such as four-wheel steering, active suspension and traction control. For the technology to be successful, a typical driver must be able to respond correctly in various driving conditions. The driver sits in a mock-up of a vehicle and drives the simulator just like a real car. The engineers can create different conditions using computer software.

The next step is to use computers to control intelligent vehicles that react to road and traffic conditions to keep cars spaced further apart than the minimum stopping distance and set the cruise speed. Further in the future is the possibility of automatic lane changing to improve the flow of traffic.

Exploration 5.6 involves a model of traffic flow that is much simpler than the systems that the motor companies are working with, but it does produce some interesting results. If you have used spreadsheet software before you should find the model very easy to follow. Carrying out this exploration may give you ideas for other models you can produce using spreadsheets. The spreadsheet software you use may be slightly different from the one that is described, but most are quite similar.

Exploration 5.6   Computer modelling of traffic flow

1 HOUR

Apparatus:

◆ spreadsheet software such as Microsoft Excel

The spreadsheet calculates the effect of a bottleneck like the one shown in Figure 5.9. This depends upon a number of different factors, all of which you can change very easily. These variables are:

- the number of lanes before the bottleneck
- the speed of the traffic approaching the bottleneck
- the number of cars per unit time approaching the bottleneck
- the number of lanes after the bottleneck
- the speed of the traffic that is clear of the bottleneck.

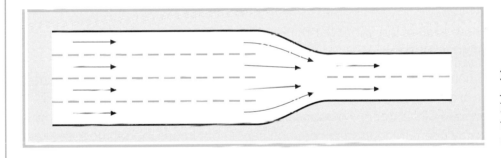

Figure 5.9
A typical bottleneck and the makings of a long tail-back

Figure 5.10 overleaf shows some values for each of these in 'cells' D1 down to D5. Cells A1 down to A5 contain the text explaining each of these variables, including the units. (*Note:* 30 m s^{-1} = 108 km h^{-1} and 15 m s^{-1} = 54 km h^{-1}).

If the spreadsheet hasn't already been written for you it is very easy to do it yourself. Open a new spreadsheet document – the one illustrated in Figure 5.10 is in Excel. Start with the text and numbers in cells A1 to A5 and D1 to D5, and then fill in the rest of the text cells: A7, A8, A10, A11, A12, A17, B17, C17 and E3.

A19, B19 and C19 all contain the number zero.

The rest of the cells contain equations:

D3 = D1*D2*D7   * means 'times'. This is the maximum 'safe' flow, but you can use a higher value in cell D3

D7 = 1/(0.1*D2*D2 + 2) the reciprocal of the minimum stopping distance

D8 = 1/(0.1*D5*D5 + 2)   this is assumed to depend on the speed squared so it is proportional to the car's kinetic energy

D10 = D4*D5*D8   flow = no. of lanes × speed × no. of cars per unit length

D11 = MIN(D10; D3)   the flow out cannot exceed the flow in

D12 = D3 − D11   ideally this is zero, then no tail-back forms

A20 = A19 + 1   Time increases in 1 s steps as you go down the column

B20 = D$12   The $ fixes the following number to '12'

C20 = (0.1*0.5*D$2*D$2 + 2)*B20

A21 = A20 + 1

B21 = D$12 + B20

C21 = (0.1*0.5*D$2*D$2 + 2)*B21

The contents of cells in columns A, B and C from rows 21 to 119 are identical except that the cell numbers in the formulae that are not preceded by a $ increase by one each time. It isn't necessary to type them all in, just select cells A21, B21 and C21 and 'fill down' to A119, B119 and C119 – you may need to refer to the instructions for your software.

If your software supports it, you can produce a graphical illustration of the results. Figure 5.11 shows the result of having just one lane after the bottleneck. The number of cars in the tail-back increases rapidly, as does the length of the tail-back.

Now investigate how each of the variables changes the traffic flow – remember, you want to avoid getting a tail-back.

It is interesting to note that increasing the speed limit after the bottle-neck can produce a tail-back. If cars are travelling quickly they should be more spaced out, this reduces the maximum flow rate of the traffic. So imposing a speed limit can improve traffic flow if it is obeyed, this may seem to contradict common sense, but in this model the safe stopping distance depends on the speed of the car squared (as does the kinetic energy of the car).

You might like to consider what speed gives the best throughput of traffic. Remember that the separation between vehicles should be the total stopping distance for the speed.

Write down a few other conclusions that you can draw by using this computer model.

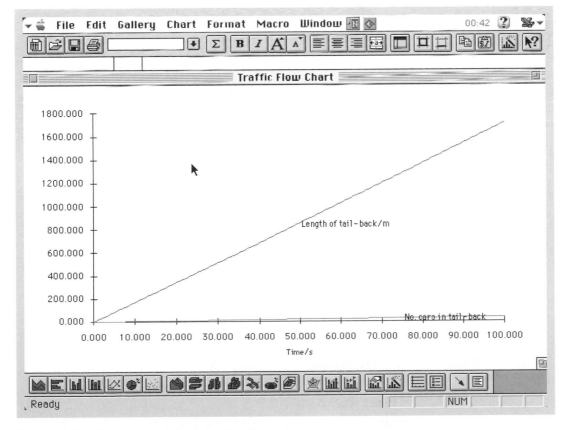

Figure 5.10 A sample spreadsheet

The following is a reconstruction of the spreadsheet shown in Figure 5.10:

	A	B	C	D	E	F	G	H
1	Number of lanes before bottleneck			3				
2	Speed prior to bottleneck/metres per sec			30.000				
3	Flow before bottleneck/cars per sec			0.978	Max =	0.978		
4	Number of lanes after bottleneck			1				
5	Speed after bottleneck/metres per sec			15.000				
6								
7	Max. no. of cars per metre before bottleneck			0.011				
8	Max.no. of cars per metre after bottleneck			0.041				
9								
10	Max flow after bottleneck			0.612				
11	Actual flow after bottleneck			0.612				
12	Flow difference = rate cars become affected			0.366				
13								
14								
15								
16								
17	Time	Number of	Length of road					
18		affected cars	affected/m					
19	0.000	0.000	0.000					
20	1.000	0.366	17.190					
21	2.000	0.732	34.381					
22	3.000	1.097	51.571					
23	4.000	1.463	68.762					
24	5.000	1.829	85.952					
25	6.000	2.195	103.143					
26	7.000	2.560	120.333					
27	8.000	2.926	137.524					

Figure 5.11 The tail-back before a bottleneck

5.4 Economizing on road transport

Given that using road transport creates such large-scale environmental problems, perhaps we should be looking for suitable alternatives. Although it may sound revolutionary now to suggest expanding the railway system so that almost nowhere in England is further than five miles from a railway station, this is exactly how it was before 1930, and almost everyone and everything got around by train – see Figure 5.12.

Contrary to popular belief, though, there has been little reduction in total rail *passenger* transport, simply a huge expansion in private car use. Lorries have, however, taken an enormous bite out of rail freight.

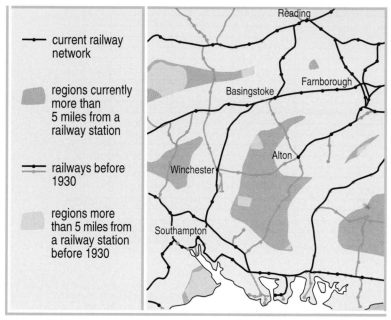

current railway network

regions currently more than 5 miles from a railway station

railways before 1930

regions more than 5 miles from a railway station before 1930

Figure 5.12
Railway network in southern England before 1930 and today

Table 5.1 UK transport modes in 1994 (ignores international traffic)

	Passenger km $\times 10^6$ yr	Freight/ Mt km yr^{-1}*	Energy consumption/10^{15} J
Air	5000	–	316
Rail	35 000	13 300	72*
Bus	43 000	–	
Motorcycle	4000	–	
Other vehicles	600 000	133 000	1545
Cycle	5000	–	
Waterborne	–	52 200	50
Pipeline	–	11 600	2
Total	692 000	210 100	1985

* Adjusted for generating losses.

Source: Based on data from Central Statistical Office, *Annual Abstract of Statistics, 1995, UK.*

Q7 Look at Table 5.1. A transport minister proposes that rail should double its carriage of both passengers and freight by transferring the following to trains: (i) the 5000×10^6 passenger km currently travelled by air, (ii) 13 300 Mt km of freight from lorries, (iii) $30\,000 \times 10^6$ passenger km from cars. Car sharing and cycling are also promoted so that car use falls in total by the same percentage as lorry use. (*Hint:* This means that total car plus lorry use falls by 10%.)

(a) How many million car passenger km will be saved in total? (b) Estimate the energy savings, both in joules and as a percentage, if these policies are successfully implemented. Comment on the plausibility of your answers. ◆

Table 5.2 Journeys per person per year in the UK and main modes of transport, 1993–5

	<5 miles	5–25 miles	>25 miles	All	Distance per person per year/miles
Walk or cycle	324	1	0	325	207
Car/van/ motorcycle	367	217	38	622	5353
Bus	48	17	1	66	362
Taxi/private hire minibus	10	2	0	12	146
Train	2	11	4	17	375
Total	751	248	43	1042	6443

 Besides saving energy, what other advantages and disadvantages are there to reducing car use?

Oil resources used in road building and coal used in steel making for the car industry could be saved (these are often referred to as capital energy costs as opposed to running costs). Other materials used in road building could also be saved, and reduced road building would mean less damage to the countryside. Moderating the use of private cars is much more effective at reducing pollution than exhaust emission controls. With fewer cars there would be fewer road accidents.

In the UK, 4000 people, 1500 of whom are pedestrians, are killed each year on the roads (this is one death per 5×10^6 passenger miles). Taking into account loss of life, loss of earnings through congestion, pollution, noise irritation, etc., the Green economist David Pearce has evaluated the cost to society of road transport at £46–53 billion per year. Others estimate it at nearer £100 billion. Tax, car parking charges, insurance premiums, etc., bring in only £29 billion – fuel ought to cost £15 per gallon (£3.30 per litre) to make up the difference! The unequal basis on which road and rail compete is shown by the fact that road receives 40 times the subsidy of rail but carries only 15 times the people and tonnage.

Attitudes towards car and other transport use are very different from country to country: in Tokyo, for example, more people cycle to work than drive; in US cities 3% of travel is on public transport while in Tokyo the figure is 67%.

Exploration 5.7   Survey of commuting habits

Do a survey on the commuting habits of the staff and students currently at your college or school, and also at the local junior school. Consider the implications for energy consumption and quality of life of a return to public transport, walking and cycling. Don't forget tlo include the effects on jobs and on those people that do not have access to a car.

Data analysis exercise – the cost of running a car

For a 1400 cc petrol car, the running costs per mile in 1996 were:

Annual mileage	Cost per mile/p
10 000	31.62
15 000	27.16
20 000	26.31
25 000	25.80

(a) Suppose that motoring costs are composed of a fixed annual cost, c (whether journeys are made or not), and a uniform cost per mile, m. By plotting a suitable graph: (i) estimate c and m, (ii) find the cost of motoring 18 000 miles, (iii) find the cost of motoring 100 000 miles.

Is this last answer justified?

(b) Railway travel costs approximately 14p per mile (budget fares), whatever the distance travelled. Using a graphical method, find out for what annual mileages is it better to own a car (i) for one person, (ii) for a couple. ◆

Bike culture (Source: painted by David Eccles, first appeared on the cover of *Bike Culture Quarterly*, available from Open Road Publishing, The Raylor Centre, James Street, York YO1 3DW)

Achievements

After working through this section you should be able to:

- explain the limiting factors associated with the efficiency of motor vehicles
- calculate the efficiencies of mechanical and electrical systems
- describe experiments on friction and say what dynamic and static friction are
- describe measures being taken to minimize the environmental impact of motor vehicles
- list some of the ways waste can be turned into useful energy
- calculate variables associated with potential dividers
- use a spreadsheet to model simple dynamic problems such as traffic flow
- compare costs of travelling by car, train, walking and cycling.

Glossary

Drag   A body moving through a fluid (gas or liquid) experiences a force parallel to its motion but in the opposite direction that tends to slow down the body if it is not compensated for by a driving force. The size of the force depends on the properties of the fluid and the moving body and on the square of body's velocity.

Dynamic frictional force   The minimum force required to maintain constant relative motion between two bodies.

Electrical conductivity   The reciprocal of resistivity. If the dimensions of an electrical conductor are kept constant, the resistance of the conductor depends directly on the resistivity. So if conductivity increases the resistance gets less.

Friction   The force acting on both of two solid bodies opposing the relative motion of the surfaces in contact. See also *Static frictional force, Dynamic frictional force, Rolling friction.*

Potentiometer   A variable resistor with three contacts: one to each end of the fixed resistance track and the third to a contact that can slide from one end of the resistance track to the other. Potentiometers are used to produce variable voltages.

Resistivity   Unit: ohm metre (Ω m). The resistance of unit length of material with uniform unit cross-sectional area, e.g. the resistance of a 1 m length of metal with a cross-sectional area of 1 m^2.

Rolling friction   Energy is used to compress the part of a pneumatic tyre that approaches the road while the wheel is rotating. Some of this energy is recovered when the tyre expands on its way up from the road, the rest is lost as heat – this energy loss process is called rolling friction.

Semiconducting materials   Materials that are neither electrical conductors nor insulators, they have *resistivities* that fall between the ranges associated with conductors and insulators. The resistivity of these materials can be changed by increasing or decreasing the number of charge carriers in the material – this can be achieved by altering the flow of energy into the material as light, thermal energy, chemical processes, etc.

Static frictional force   The minimum force required to initiate relative motion of two bodies.

Super-plastic forming   A means of joining parts of structures at high temperatures and pressures

Answers to Ready to Study test

R1

(a)

$W = Fs$

$= 1000\,\text{N} \times 100\,\text{m}$

$= 1.0 \times 10^5\ \text{J}$

(b)

$E_\text{k} = \dfrac{1}{2}mv^2$

$= 0.5 \times 1000\,\text{kg} \times 100\,\text{m}^2\,\text{s}^{-2}$

$= 0.5 \times 10^5\ \text{J}$

(c)

$\text{Efficiency} = \dfrac{\text{useful energy out}}{\text{energy in}}$

$= \dfrac{0.5 \times 10^5\ \text{J}}{1.0 \times 10^5\ \text{J}}$

$= 0.5 \text{ or } 50\%$

R2

$E_\text{k} = \dfrac{1}{2}mv^2$

$= mg\Delta h$

$= 10.0\,\text{kg} \times 9.81\,\text{N}\,\text{kg}^{-1} \times 5.00\,\text{m}$

$= 491\,\text{J}$

So

$v^2 = \dfrac{2 \times 491\,\text{J}}{10.0\,\text{kg}}$

and

$v = \sqrt{\dfrac{2 \times 491\,\text{J}}{10.0\,\text{kg}}}$

$= 9.9\,\text{ms}^{-1}$

R3

(a) $P = VI$

so

$I = \dfrac{P}{V}$

$= \dfrac{60\,\text{W}}{240\,\text{V}}$

$= 0.25\,\text{A}$

(b)

$P = \dfrac{E}{t}$

so

$t = \dfrac{E}{P}$

$= \dfrac{4.8 \times 10^4\ \text{J}}{60\,\text{W}}$

$= 800\,\text{s}$

R4

$I = \dfrac{V}{R}$

$= \dfrac{15\,\text{V}}{50\,\Omega}$

$= 0.3\,\text{A}$

Potential difference across $10\,\Omega = 0.3\,\text{A} \times 10\,\Omega$

$= 3.0\,\text{V}$

Potential difference across $40\,\Omega = 0.3\,\text{A} \times 40\,\Omega$

$= 12\,\text{V}$

Answers to questions in the text

Q1

Efficiency is given by

$$\varepsilon = 1 - \frac{1}{r^{\gamma-1}}$$

so

$$\text{original efficiency} = 1 - \frac{1}{10^{1.30-1}}$$
$$= 0.50$$

and

$$\text{improved efficiency} = 1 - \frac{1}{10^{1.35-1}}$$
$$= 0.55$$

Therefore

$$\text{improvement} = 100 \times \frac{0.55 - 0.50}{0.50}$$
$$= 10\%$$

Q2

You should have found in Exploration 5.3 that the frictional force is independent of the area of contact of the surfaces, but it is proportional to the force pressing the two surfaces together – the weight of the block, mg, in this case.

So, the force required to cause the block to slide is given by

$F = kmg$

where k is a constant for the surfaces. So

$$k \times g = \frac{F}{m}$$
$$= \frac{0.18\,\text{N}}{0.04\,\text{kg}}$$
$$= 4.5\,\text{N}\,\text{kg}^{-1}$$

(a)

$$F = 4.5\,\text{N}\,\text{kg}^{-1} \times 0.04\,\text{kg}$$
$$= 0.18\,\text{N}$$

(b)

$$F = 4.5\,\text{N}\,\text{kg}^{-1} \times (0.04 + 0.09)\,\text{kg}$$
$$= 0.59\,\text{N (to two significant figures)}$$

Q3

(a)

$$\log R = 10 + 0.5\log\left(1.0 \times 10^{-8}\right)$$
$$= 6$$

so

$$R = 1 \times 10^{6}\,\Omega$$

(b)

$$\log R = 10 + 0.5\log\left(5.0 \times 10^{-18}\right)$$
$$= 1.349$$

so

$$R = 22.4\,\Omega$$

Q4

$$V = 12V \times \frac{1000\,\Omega}{1000\,\Omega + R}$$

(a) $V = 1.20 \times 10^{-2}$ V

(b) $V = 11.7$ V

Q5

Area of peak in the region up to 2.000 minutes

$A_1 \approx 0.5 \times 2.000$ min $\times 1.000$ normalized unit (i.e. area of triangle)

$= 1.000$ unit

Area in region 2.000 to 3.000 minutes

$A_2 = 1.000 \times 0.025$

$= 0.025$ units

Total area for the first 3.000 minutes

$A_1 + A_2 = 1.025$ units

Area from 3.000 minutes to 1 hour

$A_3 = 0.025 \times 57$

$= 1.425$ units

Total area up to 1 hour

$A_1 + A_2 + A_3 = 1.025 + 1.425$

$= 2.450$ units

Proportion of hydrocarbon emissions in first 3.000 minutes

$$\frac{A_1 + A_2}{A_1 + A_2 + A_3} = \frac{1.025}{2.450}$$

$= 0.42$ or 42%

Q6

(a)

$$I = \frac{P}{V}$$

$$= \frac{E}{Vt}$$

$$= \frac{7.5 \times 10^4 \, J}{12 \, V \times 20 \, s}$$

$= 3.1 \times 10^2$ A (to two significant figures)

(b)

$mc\Delta T = 7.5 \times 10^2$ J

so

$$C = \frac{7.5 \times 10^2 \, J}{375 \, K}$$

$= 2.0 \, J \, K^{-1}$

(c)

Energy required by catalyst $= 200 \, K \times 2.0 \, J \, K^{-1}$

$= 400 \, J$

Heat that must be supplied $= 400 \, J \times \dfrac{100}{0.25}$

$= 1.6 \times 10^5$ J

Heating time $= \dfrac{1.6 \times 10^5 \, J}{12 \, V \times 3.1 \times 10^2 \, A}$

$= 43\,s$ (to two significant figures)

(d) At 1% efficiency

useful energy $= \dfrac{1}{100} \times 7.5 \times 10^4$ J

$= 7.5 \times 10^2$ J

So

power needed $= \dfrac{7.5 \times 10^2 \, J}{20 \, s}$

$= 37.5\,W$

Microwave power $= 50$ W

so

efficiency $= \dfrac{37.5 \, W}{50 \, W} \times 100$

$= 75\%$

Q7

(a) If car use falls by 10% of $600\,000 \times 10^6$ passenger km, this reduction is $60\,000 \times 10^6$ passenger km. Since $30\,000 \times 10^6$ passenger km is transferred to trains, a further $30\,000 \times 10^6$ passenger km must have been saved by cycle use and /or car sharing.

(b) Total saving $= 90\,000 \times 10^6$ passenger km.

$$\frac{13\,300\,\text{Mt km}}{133\,000\,\text{Mt km}} = 10\% \text{ as given in the question.}$$

Road traffic reductions should save about 10% of its energy consumption, which is an approximate fall of 154.5×10^{15} J. (Although this depends on the efficiency of the vehicles that reduce consumption and whether more miles are driven to pick up car sharers or deliver loads to rail heads.)

If, as the transport minister proposes, rail doubles its carriage of people and goods, then its energy consumption is likely to double (unless there is spare capacity or different efficiency motive power is used) – an increase of 72×10^{15} J.

If air travel ceases, 316×10^{15} J will be saved.

$$\text{Total saving} = (154.5 + 316 - 72) \times 10^{15} \text{ J}$$
$$= 398.5 \times 10^{15} \text{ J}$$

or

$$\frac{398.5 \times 10^{15} \text{ J}}{1985 \times 10^{15} \text{ J}} = 20\%$$

All these savings are dependent on people responding to the policy.

Solution to data analysis exercise on p. 108

(a) Let y be the total annual cost and x the mileage, then

$$y = mx + c$$

A graph of total annual cost against mileage should be approximately a straight line of gradient m and intercept c on the y axis (see Figure 5.13).

The total annual costs can be calculated (see Table 5.3).

Table 5.3

Miles per year/1000	Cost per mile/p	Annual cost/£
10	31.62	3162
15	27.16	4074
20	26.31	5262
25	25.80	6450

(i) From the graph, $c \approx £1000$ and $m \approx 22$p/mile.

(ii) From the graph, this is about £5000.

(iii) £23 000. This last answer makes the assumption that the straight line can simply be extended (or *extrapolated*). This may not be the case.

(b) (i) By train, for one person 0 miles cost 0p and 10 000 miles cost 140 000p (£1400).

A straight line is drawn through these two points to give the lower line on the graph shown in Figure 5.13.

(ii) For a couple 0 miles cost 0p and 10 000 miles cost 280 000p (£2800).

Another straight line is drawn through these points. The car and single train traveller lines don't intersect, so trains are always cheaper for one person. Depending on how you

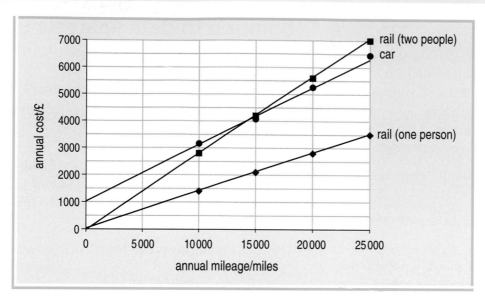

Figure 5.13 Total annual cost of car and rail travel versus mileage

have plotted your graph, the 'car' and the 'rail (two people)' lines cross at about 14 000 miles, so train is cheaper up to around 14 000 miles for two people.

All animals except humans and some of our domesticated animals survive without using fossil fuels. They can do this because they have evolved to live within the natural energy levels of their environment. They may avoid the effects of extreme weather conditions by migrating, sheltering or hibernating. They exploit the fact that Earth and the Sun have for millions of years been in a thermodynamic equilibrium, which results in conditions suitable for life for most species somewhere in the biosphere. It is to our shame that we may have disturbed this equilibrium and threatened the survival not only of animals and plants, but of ourselves too. The aim of this section is to help you gain an understanding of this thermodynamic equilibrium.

READY TO STUDY TEST

Before you begin this section you should be able to:

■ recall the modes of heat transfer and describe the process of convection

■ identify the constituents of the electromagnetic radiation spectrum and their sources, describe how they can be detected and give their typical wavelengths

■ recall and use the formula relating wavelength, frequency and wave speed

■ explain the idea of an inverse square law

■ recall the relative movement of the Sun, Earth and Moon and outline how these movements produce the seasons and cycles of day and night

■ explain the idea of a change of state

■ give the definition of pressure.

QUESTIONS

R1 (a) List in order of decreasing frequency the types of radiation in the electromagnetic spectrum. Then create and complete a table with the following headings: type of radiation, frequency range, wavelength range, source/origin, identifying characteristics, detected by, applications.

(b) What do all forms of electromagnetic radiation have in common?

R2 The intensity of radiant energy detected at a point some distance from a domestic fire is 200 W m^{-2} what would be the value of this (a) twice as far away, (b) five times as far away? Assume the fire is a point source.

THE SOLAR CONSTANT

R3 Approximately how frequently does Earth rotate on its axis?

R4 How frequently does Earth orbit the Sun?

R5 Sketch a diagram showing the orientation of the Sun and Earth that helps to explain the seasons.

R6 How frequently does the Moon orbit Earth?

R7 Write down the relationship between pressure, force and area and specify the SI units of pressure.

R8 Explain what is meant by 'a change of state' (also known as 'change of phase') by giving several examples of different kinds.

6.1 Black body radiation

Powered by thermonuclear fusion, the Sun is the prime source of energy for the Earth. By the time it reaches Earth's surface, however, solar energy is highly diffuse and varies greatly over time and from place to place. This restricts its use as an energy source. In this section we are going to look at the physics that describes and explains these features, and at the thermal radiation of hot bodies, including the Sun. But first some history.

One of the first people to attempt physical explanations of meteorological effects was John Tyndall (1820–93), who had worked as a surveyor and civil engineer in Ireland. He went on to become the director of the Royal Institution. He did much work on heat and on glaciers (he was one of the earliest people to climb the Matterhorn) and was the first to realize that the sky is blue because of **atmospheric scattering** of the Sun's spectrum. He investigated thermal radiation using an electrically heated platinum wire in a similar way to that described in the following exploration.

Exploration 6.1 Thermal radiation from a wire filament

20 MINUTES

The filament becomes very hot and can break and fall

Apparatus:

- resistance wire ◆ high-current power supply ◆ glass rod
- hand-held spectrometer (optional)

Wind a filament from your resistance wire round a glass rod and connect the ends of the wire to the output terminals of a variable, high-current supply fitted with a current trip. Increase the current slowly until the filament warms up. Notice that you can feel the warmth from the wire without the wire glowing visibly – this is infrared radiation. Notice also how a convection current develops – it is hotter above the wire than below and images are distorted in the air current. Now increase the current until the wire glows slightly. Note the colour as you continue to increase current. (You may also like to observe the spectrum of radiation emitted using a hand-held spectrometer.) Eventually the wire will fail.

 Why does the wire fail?

The wire attains a temperature at which the rate that electrical energy is supplied to the wire equals the rate that thermal energy leaves it. This is called the equilibrium temperature. When the equilibrium temperature exceeds the melting point, or the wire burns through by reacting with air, the wire breaks.

Josef Stefan (1835–93) was the son of illiterate Austrian shopkeepers. He became a schoolteacher and carried out research in his spare time, ultimately becoming a professor at Vienna University. He used Tyndall's results from his thermal radiation experiment to show that the rate of thermal radiation emission was proportional to T^4, where T is the temperature in kelvin of the radiating surface. From this, he went on to determine the first satisfactory estimate of the Sun's surface temperature.

A student of Stefan's, Ludwig Boltzmann (1844–1906), derived the 'fourth power' law described above using **kinetic theory** and thermodynamics. Unfortunately, he was prone to depression and killed himself while on holiday on the Adriatic, depressed by the lack of acceptance of his work.

This 'fourth power' law became known as the **Stefan–Boltzmann law** and can be expressed as: radiated power, $P = \varepsilon \sigma A T^4$, where A is the area radiating, T is the temperature in kelvin, ε is a measure of the effectiveness of the body at radiating, and lies between 0 and 1, and σ is Stefan's constant (5.7×10^{-8} W m^{-2} K^{-4}).

 If T doubles, what happens to the radiated power, P?

It rises to 16 times its previous value.

Gustav Kirchhoff (1824–87), a German physicist, is mainly known for his circuit theory laws, but he also developed the concept of a **black body** – a perfect radiator of thermal energy. (For a black body $\varepsilon = 1$.) He also determined the chemical elements in the Sun using spectral methods, with his friend Robert Bunsen.

ROBERT BUNSEN (1811–99)

Robert Bunsen, a German chemist, had little interest in theory, but worked with a variety of dangerous and unpleasant compounds. During this work, he lost the sight of one eye and nearly died of arsenic poisoning. He probably didn't invent the burner though. It was most likely devised by his technician, Peter Desdega, based on a design of Faraday's.

Wilhelm Wien (1864–1928) won a Nobel prize in 1896 for his discovery of the energy distribution formula for **black body radiation**, showing that $\lambda_{E\max}T = \text{constant} = 2.9 \text{ mm K}$, where $\lambda_{E\max}$ is the wavelength at which the energy output is at a maximum for a given temperature T. **Wien's law** (also called Wien's displacement law) can be expressed as:

The wavelength at which radiative power is a maximum is inversely proportional to absolute temperature, or

$$\lambda_{E\max} \propto \frac{1}{T}$$

WIEN'S LAW
The wavelength at which radiative power is a maximum is inversely proportional to absolute temperature, or

$\lambda_{E\max} \propto 1/T$

Q1 What is the wavelength at which maximum radiation occurs: (a) at 6000 K, (b) at 300 K? ◆

Q2 What temperature radiator would provide maximum radiation output within each of ultraviolet, visible, infrared and microwave? Add these to the table you drew up for R2. (Note that these temperatures don't need to be achieved for such radiation to occur. For example, a grill at 1000 K can still glow visibly red while most radiation is emitted in the infrared.) ◆

 What effect does doubling the temperature of the radiator have on the wavelength and **frequency** at which peak radiation occurs?

If T doubles, wavelength halves and frequency doubles.

 Express Wien's law in terms of frequency.

For waves of length λ and frequency f, velocity of light, $c = f \times \lambda$.

For peak radiation

$$c = f_{Emax} \times \lambda_{Emax}$$

Since

$$\lambda_{Emax} = \frac{2.9 \, mm \, K}{T}$$

according to Wien's law

$$\lambda_{Emax} = \frac{c}{f_{Emax}}$$

$$= \frac{2.9 \, mm \, K}{T}$$

$$f_{Emax} = \frac{cT}{2.9 \, mm \, K}$$

As you can see, Figure 6.1 puts together several of the laws. Look at the plotted curve for the lowest temperature and you will see that it radiates over wavelengths from 10^3 to 10^6 nm but peaks at about 10^4 nm.

The rate of energy output has a maximum for one particular value of wavelength (as given by Wien's law), but the strength of the output decreases for wavelengths either side of this value.

If the temperature of the source increases, the total output also increases (this is Stefan's law) and there is a decrease in the wavelength at which energy output peaks. A consequence is that when sufficiently hot, instead of radiating in the infrared region, visible light will be emitted, initially

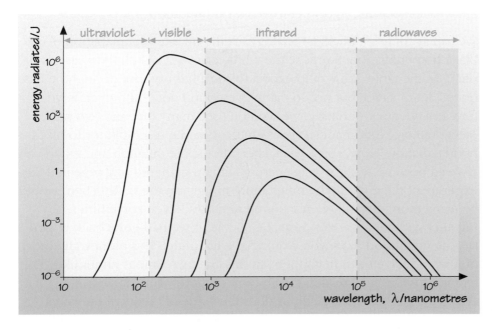

Figure 6.1
Black body radiation spectra for bodies at various temperatures

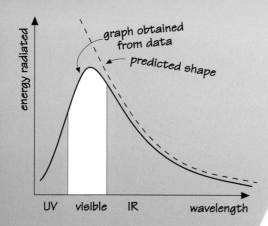

energy radiated

graph obtained from data

predicted shape

UV visible IR wavelength

Figure 6.2
The ultraviolet catastrophe

red; hotter still and the colour becomes yellower until all visible wavelengths are emitted – the surface is said to be white hot. Hotter surfaces then appear blue as this wavelength becomes more abundant.

Most of the Sun's radiation is in the visible, infrared and ultraviolet parts of the spectrum. (It is, of course, no coincidence that the Sun's energy should be just of the type with which earthly creatures see. Evolution has caused them to adjust to the most abundant radiation – and to remain highly sensitive to the effects of unusual radiations like high-frequency ultraviolet and gamma-rays).

Wien's formula for radiation from the Sun enabled the spectrum to be described but not explained. No one had a satisfying theory. Lord Rayleigh (John Strutt) and the British astrophysicist Sir James Jeans could explain the spectrum at low frequencies using classical physics, but not at high frequencies. This produced a so-called **ultraviolet catastrophe** for physics: classical theory predicted an increasing energy output as frequency increased or wavelength decreased, but this didn't occur. This is shown in Figure 6.2.

Max Planck (1858–1947) resolved the problem by invoking a revolutionary idea. He proposed that electromagnetic energy was **quantized** in packets called **photons**, these were not of equal energy but were more energetic the higher the frequency. Thus began quantum theory, which Einstein went on to use to explain the **photoelectric effect**. (Incidentally, Planck resigned from the Kaiser Wilhelm Institute in protest against the behaviour of the Nazis towards Jewish scientists in 1937. At end of the Second World War, the Institute was renamed the Max Planck Institute and moved to Göttingen where Planck was reappointed. Planck's ideas were highly controversial at the time.)

We can again use a financial analogy for the quantum explanation of black body radiation. Suppose the whole class got out all their cash and put it on the table. We would expect to see a fair number of pound coins, quite a lot of silver, but not so many five pound notes and even fewer tens and twenties. Similarly, we wouldn't see many one and two pence pieces either. Your financial spectrum bears some resemblance to black body radiation. Now, some years later, after some inflation and when you have all become wealthy wage earners, if you gathered and repeated the experiment there would be much more money on the table. There would be many more ten and twenty pound notes and even some fifties, together with rather fewer coins. Of course, if we had gone back in time to your childhood days, you would have had much less money and most of it would have been in coppers. In this analogy, time is rather like temperature: as it increases, the amount of money (the analogue of energy output rate) increases, as does the value of the most prevalent coin or note (analogous to the wavelength at which peak energy is emitted). Money is quantized too – you simply can't have 34.6 pence – it is not a continuous quantity. Also, large-value notes are more 'financially powerful' than low-value coins.

The emission spectrum from a hot surface may not conform to the ideal shape of Figures 6.1 and 6.2, which are for a black body. Such departures can be due to a superimposed characteristic line spectrum. Alternatively, some parts of the spectrum may not be emitted fully because of **reflectance** being high at particular wavelengths. For example, a green object appears green because it absorbs blue and red light well while reflecting (i.e. not absorbing) green light. According to Kirchhoff, it therefore emits blue and red wavelengths well and green poorly. The good news is that even non-black bodies can approximate to black bodies fairly closely.

 If a body at temperature T radiates into an atmosphere at temperature T_0, the net radiated heat loss rate $P \propto (T^4 - T_0^4)$. If T is much greater than T_0, which term can be neglected?

The T_0 term can be neglected.

But if T is approximately equal to T_0 the Stefan–Boltzmann law collapses into $P \propto (T - T_0)$. Remember from your algebra:

$$a^4 - b^4 = \left(a^2 + b^2\right)\left(a^2 - b^2\right)$$
$$= \left(a^2 + b^2\right)(a+b)(a-b)$$

If $a \approx b$ the first two brackets in the second line of this equation are approximately equal to $4a^3$, which may be considered fairly constant, compared with $(a - b)$. Hence

$$T^4 - T_0^4 \approx \text{constant} \times \left(T - T_0\right)$$

if $T \approx T_0$

$P \propto (T - T_0)$ is known as **Newton's law of cooling**. It holds for small differences between a body and still surroundings or large temperature differences under **forced convection**, i.e. if the fluid surroundings are moved. (An adjustment to the law, discovered by Dulong and Petit,

$$P \propto (T - T_0)^{5/4}$$

holds for higher temperature differences under **natural convection**.)

In unforced convection, a fluid is heated causing expansion and a resultant decrease in density. The warm, less dense, fluid will be buoyant; it will naturally rise and colder fluid will fall to replace it. This motion results in a convection current.

An example of forced convection is the use of a fan in conjunction with a car radiator, or the cooling of a cyclist as she moves through the air.

An example of unforced convection is dinner cooling on the table.

 Why do we often get frosts on mornings following clear night skies?

The absence of cloud allows thermal radiation directly into space from Earth's surface and warm air to rise freely forming a convection current.

 While you are busy, a friend pours your coffee which you prefer both hot and with milk. You can only get to it after several minutes. Should your friend pour the cold milk (from the fridge) in now or wait till you are ready to drink the coffee?

The rate of cooling of the drink is a function of the difference between its temperature and that of its surroundings. Black coffee will cool more quickly at its higher temperature. When the milk is poured in, it will cool even more, so your friend should pour the milk in now. (See Figure 6.3.) Furthermore, the greater body of the coffee and milk mixture cools more slowly and evaporation will be reduced from the generally lower temperature mixture.

 Exploration 6.2   Cooling curves

1 HOUR

Beware of dripping boiling water and steam

Apparatus:

(The following shapes and sizes of aluminium objects are recommended. They should all be of the same mass) ◆ aluminium plate, 50 mm × 50 mm × 6.25 mm, oriented vertically ◆ aluminium plate, 50 mm × 50 mm × 6.25 mm, oriented horizontally ◆ aluminium cube, 25 mm, painted black ◆ bare aluminium cube, 25 mm ◆ aluminium cube, 25 mm, with polystyrene jacket ◆ water bath ◆ Bunsen burner ◆ thermometers

Sockets can be drilled for thermometers, probes and suspension threads.

Heat equal mass aluminium blocks of different shapes, orientation and surface area in boiling water. Allow the blocks to cool, with one block placed in its polystyrene jacket, and plot cooling curves with common axis scales on overhead transparencies. Then juggle them about so that they all go through the same temperature (at a point when evaporation of residual water had ceased) at the same time and calculate and compare rates of cooling. You can do this investigation with temperature sensors, direct data collection and plotting by computer.

What order of cooling rates do you get? Draw up a table. Can you explain it?

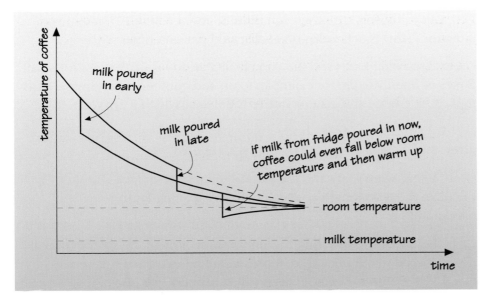

Figure 6.3
How the coffee cools over time

6.2 Radiation balance

Spectroscopy concerns the measurement of wavelengths of light, and if done through telescopes it can be used to determine the temperatures of stars. (*Note:* When answering the following questions you need to carry through values from one question to another. You should round each answer to the appropriate number of significant figures, but carry through the unrounded answers to avoid accumulating rounding errors.)

Q3 Suppose the wavelength at which the Sun's surface radiation peaks is 500 nm. Using Wien's law, calculate the surface temperature of the Sun. ◆

Q4 Using the Stefan–Boltzmann law, find the rate at which energy is radiated by the Sun, per unit area. (Assume that the Sun is a perfect black body. Stefan's constant, $\sigma = 5.7 \times 10^{-8}$ W m^{-2} K^{-4}.) ◆

Q5 Given that the Sun's radius is 6.69×10^8 m, find the total energy radiated per unit time by the Sun. ◆

Q6 Using $E = mc^2$, estimate the rate of mass loss of the Sun. ◆

The **inverse square law** tells us that the intensity of radiation I_1 at the distance r_1 from an imaginary point source is related to intensity I_0 produced at distance r_0 by

$$\frac{I_1}{I_0} = \left(\frac{r_0}{r_1} \right)^2$$

I_1 is a constant – it is the intensity of the solar radiation above Earth's atmosphere. It is called the **solar constant**.

Q7 If the radius of Earth's orbit is $r_1 = 1.5 \times 10^{11}$ and the radius of the Sun is $r_0 = 6.69 \times 10^8$ m, calculate I_1 using your value of I_0 from Question 4. ◆

123

Q8 Earth presents a disc with a radius of about 6.38×10^6 m to this radiation. How much radiation is collected per unit time?

(*Hint:* Assuming Earth and the Sun are in a steady state (except for small fluxes of energy from, for example, fossil and geothermal sources), Earth must emit energy at the same rate as the rate at which it arrives.) ◆

Q9 If Earth too is a black body, calculate its mean surface temperature, given that it emits energy all over its surface area. ◆

Q10 Using Wien's law and the surface temperature from Question 9, calculate the wavelength at which radiation leaving Earth is a maximum. ◆

Q11 Re-do Question 9, but this time assume 30% of the solar energy is not absorbed in the first place, representing reflection of solar energy by cloud, desert and ice caps. (This is called **albedo**.) ◆

Earth's temperature is higher than the answer you found in Question 9 and much higher than the answer you found in Question 11, so something is keeping Earth hotter than it 'ought' to be, either by increasing the energy arriving at the surface, or decreasing its rate of departure. Geothermal energy and fossil fuels are candidates for the first idea. In fact, though, the second idea turns out to be much more important. Earth's atmosphere reduces the rate of thermal energy loss. This is called the greenhouse effect and is responsible for maintaining a temperature that is able to support life on Earth.

The rate of energy emission by Earth equals rate of supply to it unless Earth is heating up or cooling down. The mean rate at which energy arrives at Earth's upper atmosphere can be calculated from the solar constant. This is the total energy radiated by the Sun per unit area at the mean distance from Earth. It is taken as 1.37×10^3 W m^{-2}, which you found in the answer to Question 7. In fact, the rate varies from zero to about 1400 W m^{-2}. The maximum value will occur when the Sun is overhead and when Earth is closest to the Sun. The minimum value occurs between dusk and dawn, and also during the polar nights of 6 months' duration beyond the 66° latitudes.

Figure 6.4
A ray glancing Earth's surface

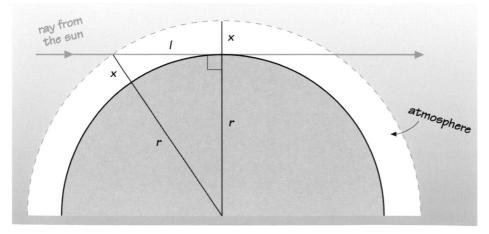

Q12 Figure 6.4 shows a ray 'glancing' Earth's surface at dawn. Taking the atmosphere's thickness, x, as 5.0×10^4 m and the radius of Earth, r, as 6.38×10^6 m, use Pythagoras'

theorem to estimate the number of atmosphere thicknesses through which these rays pass, before touching Earth's surface. ◆

Q13   Give, as a fraction of the solar energy input, (a) the world's current energy consumption, (b) the world's energy consumption if everyone lived like people in the USA do, with a world population of twice its present size. Use your answers from the data analysis exercise in Section 2. ◆

Q14   For every 4% rise in energy consumption compared with the Sun's input, Earth's temperature rises about 3 K (1% of its mean temperature). What temperature rise of Earth is associated with scenario (b) in Queston 13? (Remember, the fossil fuel is an addition to the Sun's energy input.) (*Note:* This is not the greenhouse effect; it is supplementary to it and is not disputed.) ◆

Q15   The Earth–Sun distance varies by about ±3% during the year. (a) By how much will the solar constant vary? (b) Is this sufficient to explain the seasons? Use the data in Table 6.1. ◆

Table 6.1   Radiation totals

(a) Mean monthly totals of radiation measured at Kew on a horizontal surface/kW h m^{-2}*	(b) Radiation on south-facing surfaces at angles given to horizontal/kW h m^{-2}†			
	30°	45°	60°	90°
Jan	16.7	25.0	29.2	29.2	27.8
Feb	27.9	37.5	40.3	40.3	34.2
Mar	63.6	81.9	86.1	81.9	66.7
Apr	95.7	100.0	95.8	90.3	65.3
May	136.7	133.3	126.4	115.3	79.2
June	144.6	143.0	131.9	118.1	77.8
July	136.1	131.9	125.0	111.1	73.6
Aug	115.0	120.8	115.3	105.6	76.4
Sept	84.6	97.2	97.2	93.1	73.6
Oct	48.7	65.3	69.4	68.1	58.3
Nov	20.7	33.3	36.1	37.5	34.7
Dec	12.7	23.6	26.4	27.8	26.4
Total	903.0	993.0	980.6	916.7	694.4

Sources:

* Collinbourne, R. H. (1975) Meterological Office, Bracknell, Berkshire. Conference on UK Meteorological Data and Solar Energy Applications at the Royal Institution, London. (Report by International Solar Energy Society.)

† Courtney, R. G. (1976) Building Research Establishment Report CP7/76.

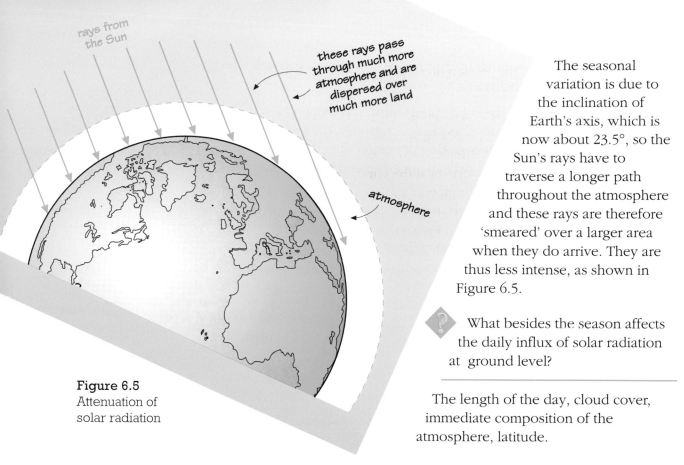

these rays pass through much more atmosphere and are dispersed over much more land

rays from the Sun

atmosphere

Figure 6.5
Attenuation of solar radiation

The seasonal variation is due to the inclination of Earth's axis, which is now about 23.5°, so the Sun's rays have to traverse a longer path throughout the atmosphere and these rays are therefore 'smeared' over a larger area when they do arrive. They are thus less intense, as shown in Figure 6.5.

? What besides the season affects the daily influx of solar radiation at ground level?

The length of the day, cloud cover, immediate composition of the atmosphere, latitude.

Because of the daily rotation of the Earth and its yearly apparent precession of its axis, the quantity of solar power incident on Earth is not only fairly *diffuse* but also highly *variable*.

Q16 Figure 6.6 shows the apparent trajectory of the Sun on a day midway between midsummer and midwinter (the equinox) in southern

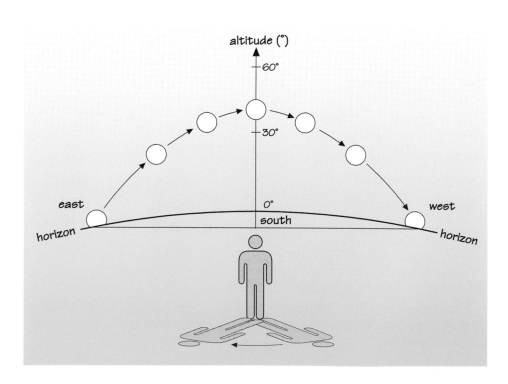

Figure 6.6
The Sun's apparent position at two-hourly intervals

England. Copy the figure and sketch on it paths for midsummer and midwinter (the solstices). ◆

During the winter, when Earth's axis is tilted away from the Sun, the day is only about 8 hours long at the UK's latitude (within the Arctic circle, there is no daylight at all). Also, the Sun is very low in the sky, never rising more than 15° above the horizon at the winter solstice, when the rays have to pass through a minimum equivalent of about four atmospheres before reaching the ground. Again, the rays are 'smeared' out over a larger area. Consequently, the power from the Sun impinging on 1 square metre (called **insolation**) ranges from 0 W m^{-2} at night to about 900 W m^{-2} at midday in Britain at midsummer. However, it reaches only about 200 W m^{-2} in midwinter, and sunlight lasts only half the time. Furthermore, the orientation of the receiving surface is important too. (See Figure 6.7 and Table 6.1.)

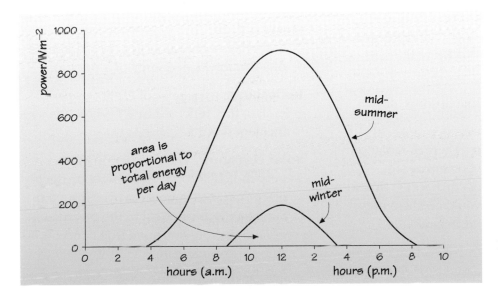

Figure 6.7
Insolation by time of day

Q17 Solar radiation at ground level on the Moon (which has no atmosphere) is 1400 W m^{-2} when the Sun is overhead. What will the radiation intensity at the surface of the Moon be for angles 60°, 30°, 0° of the Sun above the horizon? ◆

Achievements

After working through this section you should be able to:

- describe black body radiation and use Wien's law and the Stefan–Boltzmann law
- derive Newton's law of cooling
- calculate the solar constant
- describe the greenhouse effect.

Glossary

Albedo   The fraction of incident light reflected from a surface.

Atmospheric scattering   The deflection of radiation by the molecules of the atmosphere.

Black body   A body that absorbs all incident radiation.

Black body radiation   Thermal radiation spectrum from a perfect emitter (a radiator of emissivity equal to 1). This so-called black body would be absolutely dark if not emitting visible radiation.

Forced convection   A convection current stimulated and increased by the artificial removal of the rising hot air, with the use of a fan for example.

Frequency   Unit: hertz (Hz). The number of complete oscillations or cycles per unit time for a vibrating system.

Insolation   The radiation received from the Sun.

Inverse square law   A law in which one variable is inversely proportional to the square of another, e.g. Coulomb's law.

Kinetic theory   The theory that proposes that matter consists of molecules in motion having internal energy due to this motion and their relative positions.

Natural convection   The transfer of thermal energy because of the upward movement of a warm fluid resulting from decreased density after heating.

Newton's law of cooling   The rate of loss of energy of a body is proportional to the difference in temperature of the body and its surroundings.

Photoelectric effect   The emission of electrons from a material due to incident electromagnetic radiation.

Photon   The quantum of electromagnetic energy having magnitude hf, where f is its frequency and h is Planck's constant.

Quantization   The process of constructing a discrete set of values for the magnitude of a variable, e.g. energy of a photon.

Reflectance   The ratio of luminous or radiant flux reflected by a body to the incident flux.

Solar constant   The rate per unit area perpendicular to the Sun's rays at which electromagnetic energy arrives from the Sun at a distance equal to the mean radius of Earth's orbit. It is not a true constant. Its value is approximately 1370 W m^{-2}.

Stefan–Boltzmann law   The rate of emission of radiant energy per unit area of a black body (in W m^{-2}) is proportional to the fourth power of absolute temperature. It can also be expressed as radiated power, $P = \varepsilon \sigma A T^4$, where A is the area radiating, T is the temperature in kelvin, ε is a measure of the effectiveness of the body at radiating, lying between 0 and 1, and σ is Stefan's constant $(5.7 \times 10^{-8} \text{ W m}^{-2} \text{ K}^{-4})$.

Ultraviolet catastrophe   The inability of classical physics to explain the fall in intensity of (ultraviolet) radiation with decreasing wavelength of black body spectra.

Wien's law The wavelength at which the maximum of the black body spectrum curve lies is inversely proportional to the absolute temperature of the emitter surface: $\lambda_{E\max} = \dfrac{2.9 \times 10^3 \text{ mm}}{T}$

Answers to Ready to Study test

R1

(a) See Table 6.2 overleaf

(b) They all have a velocity of 3.0×10^8 m s^{-1} in a vacuum. All increase the energy of an absorber and can also be reflected, refracted and transmitted by matter to varying degrees.

R2

The inverse square law implies that

$$\frac{I_1}{I_2} = \left(\frac{R_2}{R_1}\right)^2$$

where I is intensity and R is distance.

(a) If $I_1 = 200$ W m^{-2} at R_1, using the inverse square law gives

$$\frac{200 \text{ W m}^{-2}}{I_2} = \left(\frac{2R_1}{R_1}\right)^2$$

so

$$
\begin{aligned}
I_2 &= \frac{200 \text{ W m}^{-2}}{4} \\
&= 50 \text{ W m}^{-2}
\end{aligned}
$$

(b) Intensity at five times the distance is

$$
\begin{aligned}
I_2 &= \frac{200 \text{ W m}^{-2}}{25} \\
&= 8 \text{ W m}^{-2}
\end{aligned}
$$

R3

Once every 24 hours.

R4

Once each year or 365.25 days.

R5

See Figure 6.8.

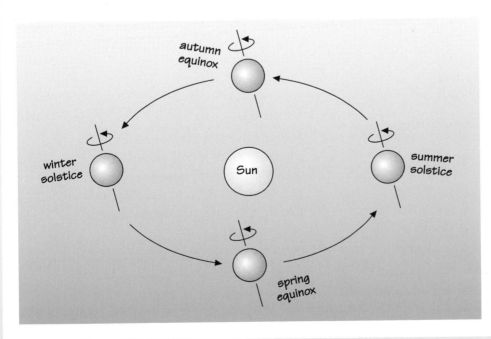

Figure 6.8
Motion of Earth about the Sun

Table 6.2 The electromagnetic spectrum

Type of radiation		Frequency range/Hz	Wavelength range/m	Source/ origin	Identifying characteristics	Detected by	Applications
γ-rays		10^{19}–10^{32}	10^{-10}–10^{-16}	nucleus	particle nature can cause cancer	GM tube phosphorescence ionization	radiotherapy
X-rays		10^{16}–10^{20}	10^{-7}–10^{-12}	energy transitions of innermost orbital electrons	penetrates low-density tissue can cause cancer	photographic film	radiography X-ray crystallography
UV		10^{15}–10^{17}	10^{-6}–10^{-9}	energy transitions of electrons Sun	causes suntan and cancer	fluorescence sunburn on skin	therapy for SAD hardening tooth fillings photo etching
visible		10^{14}	10^{-7}	energy transitions of electrons Sun	affects retina in the eye, so can be seen	eye photographic film bolometer	photography
IR		10^{11}–10^{14}	10^{-3}–10^{-6}	thermal excitation of molecules and atoms	warms absorbers	thermopile	IR spectroscopy
micro		10^{9}–10^{12}	1–10^{-4}	oscillations of electrons in transmitting aerials	causes resonance in water molecules	oscillation of molecules	microwave radio links microwave cooker
radio	S	10^{7}–10^{10}	10^{-1}–1	oscillations of electrons in transmitting aerials	causes resonance in tuned electrical circuits	resonance in tuned electrical circuits	radio communications
	M	10^{6}–10^{7}	1–10^{1}				
	L	10^{3}–10^{5}	10^{2}–10^{3}				

R6

The Moon orbits Earth approximately once a month or 29 days.

R7

$$\text{Pressure} = \frac{\text{force}}{\text{area}}$$ and it is measured in pascals, symbol Pa.

R8

Matter can exist in three main states (or phases): solid, liquid and gas (there is actually a fourth phase too, known as plasma). Changes of phase include melting, freezing, boiling, condensing and sublimation.

Answers to questions in text

Q1

$$\lambda_{Emax} = \frac{2.9\,mm\,K}{T}$$

(a) Therefore at 6000 K

$$\lambda_{Emax} = \frac{2.9\,mm\,K}{6000\,K}$$

$$= 4.8 \times 10^{-4} \text{ mm or } 4.8 \times 10^{-7} \text{ m}$$

(to two significant figures)

(b) At 300 K

$$\lambda_{Emax} = \frac{2.9\,mm\,K}{300\,K}$$

$$= 9.7 \times 10^{-3} \text{ mm or } 9.7 \times 10^{-6} \text{ m}$$

(to two significant figures)

Q2

Taking a typical ultraviolet wavelength

$$\lambda = 3 \times 10^{-8}\,m$$

and using

$$\lambda T = 2.9 \times 10^{-3}\,K\,m$$

gives

$$T = \frac{2.9 \times 10^{-3}\,K\,m}{3 \times 10^{-8}\,m}$$

$$\approx 1 \times 10^{5}\,K$$

If a black body were to emit ultraviolet radiation at the peak of its spectrum, its temperature, T, would be about 10^5 K. For visible light, $T \approx 6000$ K, for infrared $T \approx 300$ K and for microwave radiation $T \approx 3$ K.

Q3

$$\lambda_{Emax} = 500\,nm$$

$$= 5.0 \times 10^{-4}\,mm$$

Using Wien's law

$$\lambda_{Emax} = \frac{2.9\,mm\,K}{T}$$

so

$$T = \frac{2.9\,mm\,K}{5.0 \times 10^{-4}\,mm}$$

$$= 5.8 \times 10^{3}\,K \text{ (to two significant figures)}$$

Q4

The Stefan–Boltzmann law states

$$P = \varepsilon \sigma A T^{4}$$

Power radiated per unit area is

$$I_0 = \frac{P}{A}$$

$$= \varepsilon \sigma T^{4}$$

For a perfect black body $\varepsilon = 1$, so

$$I_0 = 1 \times 5.7 \times 10^{-8}\,W\,m^{-2}\,K^{-4} \times 5800^{4}\,K^{4}$$

$$= 6.450 \times 10^{7}\,W\,m^{-2}$$

$$= 6.5 \times 10^{7}\,W\,m^{-2}$$

(to two significant figures)

Q5

Surface area of the Sun is given by

$$A = 4\pi r^{2}$$

$$= 4\pi \left(6.69 \times 10^{8} \right)^{2}\,m^{2}$$

$$= 5.62 \times 10^{18}\,m^{2}$$

Total power radiated by the Sun is

$$P = I_0 \times A$$

$$= 6.45 \times 10^7 \, \text{W m}^{-2} \times 5.62 \times 10^{18} \, \text{m}^2$$

$$= 36.2 \times 10^{25} \, \text{W}$$

$$= 3.6 \times 10^{26} \, \text{W} \quad \text{(to two significant figures)}$$

Q6

From

$$E = mc^2$$

$$\text{mass loss per second} = \frac{\text{energy loss per second}}{c^2}$$

$$= \frac{3.62 \times 10^{26} \, \text{W}}{\left(3.0 \times 10^8\right)^2 \, \text{ms}^{-2}}$$

$$= 0.402 \times 10^{10} \, \text{kg s}^{-1}$$

$$= 4.0 \times 10^9 \, \text{kg s}^{-1}$$

$$\text{(to two significant figures)}$$

Q7

$$\frac{I_1}{I_0} = \left(\frac{r_0}{r_1}\right)^2$$

$$I_1 = I_0 \left(\frac{r_0}{r_1}\right)^2$$

Using

$$I_0 = 6.45 \times 10^7 \, \text{W m}^{-2}$$

from Question 4

$$I_1 = 6.45 \times 10^7 \, \text{W m}^{-2} \frac{\left(6.69 \times 10^8 \, \text{m}\right)^2}{\left(1.5 \times 10^{11} \, \text{m}\right)^2}$$

$$= 1283 \, \text{W m}^{-2}$$

$$= 1.3 \times 10^3 \, \text{W m}^{-2}$$

$$\text{(to two significant figures)}$$

The solar constant is therefore about 1300 W m^{-2}. (The current published value is actually 1370 W m^{-2}.)

Q8

Area of Earth receiving radiation from the Sun is

$$A = \pi r^2$$

$$= \pi \left(6.38 \times 10^6 \, \text{m}\right)^2$$

$$= 1.279 \times 10^{14} \, \text{m}^2$$

$$= 1.28 \times 10^{14} \, \text{m}^2 \text{(to three significant figures)}$$

Radiation energy received by Earth per second is given by

$$P = I_1 \times A$$

$$= 1283 \, \text{W m}^{-2} \times 1.279 \times 10^{14} \, \text{m}^2$$

$$= 1.641 \times 10^{17} \, \text{W}$$

$$= 1.64 \times 10^{17} \, \text{W} \quad \text{(to two significant figures)}$$

Q9

Surface area of Earth $= 4\pi r^2$

$$= 4 \times \pi \times \left(6.38 \times 10^6 \, \text{m}\right)^2$$

$$= 5.12 \times 10^{14} \, \text{m}^2$$

$$\text{(to three significant figures)}$$

Using the Stefan–Boltzmann law, $P = \varepsilon\sigma AT^4$, and substituting the values $\varepsilon = 1$ for a black body, $\sigma = 5.7 \times 10^{-8} \, \text{W m}^{-2} \, \text{K}^{-4}$ and, from the answer to Question 8, $P = 1.641 \times 10^{17} \, \text{W}$

we get

$$T^4 = \frac{P}{\varepsilon\sigma A}$$

$$= \frac{1.641 \times 10^{17} \, \text{W}}{1 \times 5.7 \times 10^{-8} \, \text{W m}^{-2} \, \text{K}^{-4} \times 5.12 \times 10^{14} \, \text{m}^2}$$

$$= 0.0562 \times 10^{11} \, \text{K}^4$$

$$= 5.62 \times 10^9 \, \text{K}^4 \quad \text{(to three significant figures)}$$

Therefore

$$T = 2.738 \times 10^2 \text{ K}$$
$$\approx 1°C$$

So the mean surface temperature is about 1°C.

Q10

Using Wien's law

$$\lambda_{E\max} = \frac{2.9 \text{ mm K}}{T}$$
$$= \frac{2.9 \text{ mm K}}{2.738 \times 10^2 \text{ K}}$$
$$= 1.059 \times 10^{-5} \text{ m}$$
$$= 1.1 \times 10^{-5} \text{ m}$$

(to two significant figures)

Q11

We now have a new value for P.

$$P = 1.641 \times 10^{17} \text{ W} \times 0.7$$
$$= 1.149 \times 10^{17} \text{ W}$$

So now

$$T^4 = \frac{P}{\varepsilon \sigma A}$$

$$= \frac{1.149 \times 10^{17} \text{ W}}{1 \times 5.7 \times 10^{-8} \text{ W m}^{-2} \text{ K}^{-4} \times 5.12 \times 10^{14} \text{ m}^2}$$

$$= 3.937 \times 10^9 \text{ K}^4$$

Therefore

$$T = 250 \text{ K}$$
$$\approx -23°C$$

So the mean surface temperature is about −23°C.

Q12

Applying Pythagoras' theorem to the triangle in Figure 6.4 gives

$$(r + x)^2 = r^2 + l^2$$
$$r^2 + 2rx + x^2 = r^2 + l^2$$

so

$$l^2 = 2rx + x^2$$
$$= (2r + x)x$$

Therefore

$$l = \sqrt{(2r + x)x}$$
$$= \sqrt{\left[2(6.38 \times 10^6 \text{ m}) + (5 \times 10^4 \text{ m})\right] \times 5 \times 10^4 \text{ m}}$$
$$= \sqrt{64.1 \times 10^{10} \text{ m}}$$
$$= 8.001 \times 10^5 \text{ m}$$

Number of atmosphere thicknesses

$$= \frac{8.001 \times 10^5 \text{ m}}{5.0 \times 10^4 \text{ m}}$$
$$= 16 \text{ (to two significant figures)}$$

Q13

(a) From Question 8, radiation energy received by Earth per second is

$1.64 \times 10^{17} \text{ J s}^{-1}$.

From the solution to the data analysis exercise in Section 2 the world's current energy consumption rate is

$$355620 \times 10^{15} \text{ J yr}^{-1} = \frac{355620 \times 10^{15}}{365 \times 24 \times 60 \times 60} \text{ J s}^{-1}$$
$$= 1.13 \times 10^{13} \text{ J s}^{-1}$$

So, world energy consumption as a fraction of solar energy input is

$$\frac{1.13 \times 10^{13}}{1.64 \times 10^{17}} = 6.89 \times 10^{-5}$$

(to three significant figures)

i.e. consumption of fossil and other fuels is a tiny fraction of total solar flux arriving at Earth.

(b) From the solution to the data analysis exercise in Section 2, world consumption at the USA per capita rate is

$$90\,203 \times 10^{15} \text{ J} \times \frac{5.29 \times 10^9}{2.60 \times 10^8} \text{ yr}^{-1}$$

$$= 1.835 \times 10^{21} \text{ J yr}^{-1}$$

With double the population, the new consumption rate would be

$$3.67 \times 10^{21} \text{ J yr}^{-1} = \frac{3.67 \times 10^{21}}{365 \times 24 \times 60 \times 60} \text{ J s}^{-1}$$

$$= 1.164 \times 10^{14} \text{ J s}^{-1}$$

As a fraction solar energy input this is

$$\frac{1.164 \times 10^{14}}{1.64 \times 10^{17}} = 7.10 \times 10^{-4}$$

(to three significant figures)

Again, this fraction is still very small.

Q14

$$\text{Percentage rise} = (7.1 \times 10^{-4}) \times 100\%$$

$$= 0.071\%$$

$$\text{Temperature rise} = \frac{0.071 \times 3 \text{ K}}{4}$$

$$= 5.3 \times 10^{-2} \text{ K}$$

Q15

(a) A variation of ±3% suggests that

$$r_{max} = 1.03 \text{ times normal}$$

and

$$r_{min} = 0.97 \text{ times normal}$$

or, approximately

$$r_{max} = 1.06 r_{min}$$

$$\frac{I_{max}}{I_{min}} = \left(\frac{r_{min}}{r_{max}}\right)^2$$

$$= \left(\frac{1}{1.06}\right)^2$$

$$= 0.890 \text{ (to three significant figures)}$$

I_{min} is approximately 10% less than I_{max}.

(b) It is not sufficient to explain the seasons. The daily solar flux varies by a factor of 12 between mid-winter and mid-summer in the UK. (In fact, the Sun and Earth are closer in our winter!)

Q16

See Figure 6.9.

Q17

See Figure 6.10. Rays of width x are smeared over length y. Therefore, because of conservation of energy

$$I_{ground} \times y = I_{sky} \times x$$

so

$$\frac{I_{ground}}{I_{sky}} = \frac{x}{y}$$

$$= \sin\theta$$

Therefore

$$I_{ground} = I_{sky} \times \sin\theta$$

$\theta / °$	$I_{ground}/\text{W m}^{-2}$
90	1400
60	1212
30	700
0	0

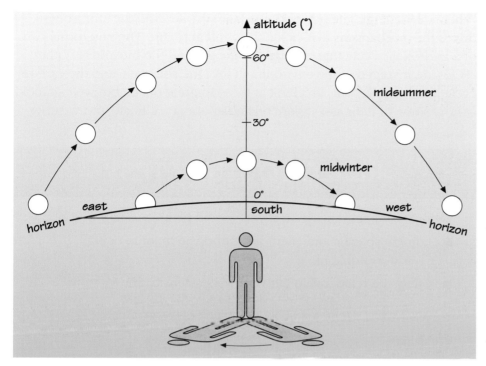

Figure 6.9
Answer to
Question 16

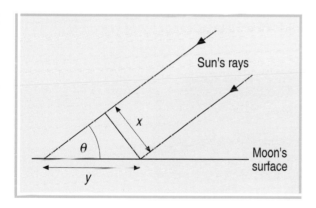

Figure 6.10 The Sun's rays 'smeared' over the
Moon's surface

7

When solar energy interacts with the land, the sea and the atmosphere, it drives the mechanisms that create the wind and rain. The rain forms part of a hydrologic cycle that circulates water around the biosphere. Other cycles are involved in the environment too: the soil cycle and the carbon cycle, for example. We can't look at these in great detail, but we can look at how some of their aspects are related to energy, climate and weather.

READY TO STUDY TEST

Before you begin this section you should be able to:

- define specific and latent heats and use them in energy transfer problems
- state the relationship between mass, density and volume.

QUESTIONS

R1 A solar house of outer perimeter length 32.0 m has concrete walls 0.50 m thick and 5.00 m high. If they cool from 30°C down to 10°C, how much thermal energy leaves them? (Density of concrete = 2700 kg m^{-3} and specific heat capacity of concrete, $c = 850$ J kg^{-1} K^{-1}.)

A solar house

R2 A different heat storage design has a tank containing 750 kg of wax (specific latent heat of fusion 1.4×10^4 J kg^{-1}) in the cellar that is melted by the Sun at 32°C through pipes connected to a heat exchanger. During the night the wax solidifies. How much thermal energy is given out during the solidification of the wax? What name is given to this thermal energy? It then cools as a solid down to 16°C. How much more thermal energy is given out? What name is given to this kind of thermal energy ? (Specific heat capacity of wax = 110 J kg^{-1} K^{-1}.)

7.1 Water: the unique molecule

Without water life would not exist. Life began in the seas some 53 million years ago, and many animals and plants can still live only in water. Our bodies are 70% water, and **photosynthesis** in plants cannot function without water. Water's importance is due to the need of every living cell to transfer chemicals to and from itself – water's ability to dissolve compounds makes cellular development possible.

Before looking at the **hydrosphere** you should revise some of the unique chemical properties of water.

Chemical properties of water

Water is composed of two hydrogen atoms and one oxygen atom held together by strong covalent bonds. A covalent bond is an electron-sharing bond. This means that each hydrogen atom shares its electron with the oxygen atom, and the oxygen atom shares one of the two electrons in its outer shell with each hydrogen atom. However, the electrons spend a longer time closer to the oxygen atom than to the hydrogen atoms, which produces a slight positive charge on the hydrogen end of the molecule and a slight negative charge on the oxygen end. Because of this, water is said to be 'polar' (it is a **polar molecule**) and acts as an **electric dipole** (see Figure 7.1).

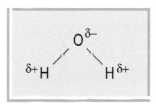

Figure 7.1
A polar water molecule

When solid, the positively charged hydrogen ends of one molecule are attracted to the negatively charged ends of the oxygen atoms in neighbouring water molecules, thus forming hydrogen bonds. These hydrogen bonds give solid water (ice) its structure and cause the water molecules to be arranged in a regular pattern or lattice (see Figure 7.2).

As ice is heated, the water molecules vibrate faster, until at 0°C they move fast enough to break free from the lattice pattern. But the hydrogen bonds are strong enough to hold the molecules together – unlike other simple molecules (such as carbon dioxide, methane and nitrous oxide), water remains liquid (rather than becoming a gas) at normal room temperature. Without these attractive hydrogen bonds, water wouldn't be liquid at the temperatures found on Earth.

Figure 7.2
Water molecules linked by hydrogen bonding

 As a liquid cools, what happens to its volume and its density?

Materials usually contract when their temperatures fall, which causes an increase in density.

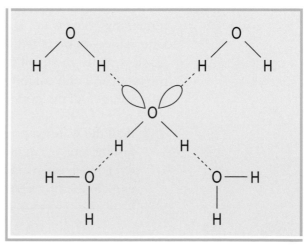

Water is unusual in this respect. It is at its most dense at 4°C (above its freezing point), which is why ice floats in water. As the temperature is lowered from 4°C, water expands, gradually at first. However, below 0°C it expands rapidly as it freezes generating sufficient force to burst pipes and split rock.

Energy is absorbed from the environment in melting or evaporating a substance and emitted into the environment when it freezes or condenses.

Q1 Back to your now cold coffee from Section 6. Your friend tries to make things up to you by taking you to a café for some hot coffee. At the café the staff heat the coffee by squirting steam at 100°C into it from a jet. In warming the drink (treat it as water for now) from 20°C to 100°C, how much steam condenses into the drink, as a proportion of the original contents? (Specific heat capacity of water, $c = 4.2 \times 10^3$ J kg^{-1} K^{-1}; latent heat of vaporization of water = 2.3×10^6 J kg^{-1}.) ◆

Q2 Your friend is from the USA where they like their cola as cool as possible. How much ice should they add to their drink to achieve this, but without using any more ice than is necessary? Treat the drink as water and give your answer as a ratio of mass of ice to mass of drink. Assume the drink starts at 15°C. (Latent heat of fusion of water = 3.34×10^5 J kg^{-1}.) ◆

Although we have been considering hot and cold drinks here, these are relevant to our topic. The weather is highly dependent on the water content of the atmosphere, and this depends on the exchanges between ice, snow, water and water vapour driven by or contributing to energy flows in the **biosphere**; these flows take the form of air and water currents.

7.2 The hydrosphere

The total volume of water on Earth has been estimated at 1384 million cubic kilometres, 97% of which is in the oceans. If this were evenly distributed it would cover Earth's surface to a depth of 2.8 km. The remaining 3% of water is at any one time in the atmosphere or on the land. Three-quarters of that 3% is retained in the polar ice caps and glaciers. Thus, the fresh water in soil, rivers and lakes is less than 1% of the total, and only an infinitesimal 0.035% is at any instant in the atmosphere. All this water together makes up the hydrosphere.

 If all the water vapour in the atmosphere was to be released at one instant, only 3 cm rainfall would be collected at Earth's surface, yet over a year an average of 90–100 cm of rain falls on Earth. Can you explain the discrepancy?

There is a constant recycling of water between the oceans and the atmosphere.

This is known as the **hydrologic cycle** (or the water cycle). Once again, it is the Sun that drives this vital mechanism. Most of the water vapour (84%) in the atmosphere comes from the oceans, **transpiration** from plants accounting for most of the remaining 16%. Figure 7.3 illustrates the features of the cycle.

The Sun heats the water in the oceans and on land surfaces, which causes evaporation. The warm moist air rises, expands under reduced pressure in the higher atmosphere and cools; water vapour then condenses to form clouds. The winds carry the clouds across Earth's surface until the water is released as precipitation (rain, hail or snow) to fall on Earth's surface for further recycling. Most of the precipitation will fall back into the oceans (three-quarters of Earth's surface being ocean) but the little that falls on land replenishes our fresh water supply and sustains life on the land.

The rate of circulation of water within the hydrologic cycle is very rapid. Since the total mass of water in the hydrosphere (water in all its forms close to Earth's surface) is constant, precipitation must, over time, be balanced by evaporation. Comparing throughputs, it is found that the evaporated water remains in the atmosphere for only ten days on average.

Figure 7.3
The hydrologic cycle

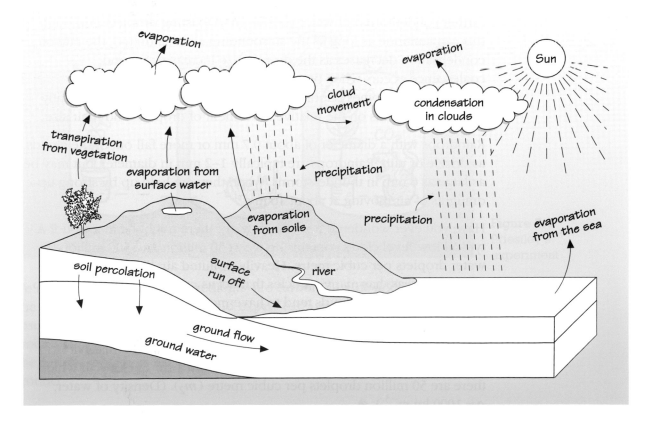

The soil

Throughout this unit we have discussed Earth's surface and atmosphere. We have noted how they are responsible for the creation of a solar **radiation balance** within the atmosphere and the maintenance of the greenhouse effect. Earth's surface is a complicated entity made up of many different surfaces, including the oceans, barren deserts, polar ice-fields, rich forest plant life and urban areas. Each of these has a different **albedo** (a fractional measure of how much light is diffusely reflected by each surface), each absorbs water at a different rate and each may be a different source or sink of gases (such as CO_2). Albedos vary from 3% for water under a 'high sun' to 95% for snow. Grassland has an albedo of 16–26%.

When we consider the land surface we categorize it by its 'soil'. The soil consists of both rock particles and organic material called 'humus', which is made up of the remains of plants and animals in various stages of decomposition. It is the humus that serves as the food for many living organisms. Animals (e.g. earthworms, ants and larvae) and plants (e.g. bacteria and fungi) in the soil break the humus down into soluble substances that can be absorbed by the roots of the larger plants. About half of the volume of the soil is filled by air and water. Soils are classified by the proportions of air, water and size of rock particles within them.

As we mentioned earlier, much of the rain falling over Earth's land surface is ultimately returned to the ocean, maintaining the balance of the hydrologic cycle. The mechanisms by which water is passed through the soil is a complex one, but one that is essential to the existence of animal and plant life. It is the passage of water through the soil that transports nutrients for plants and filters out harmful chemicals producing pure water that is safe to drink. So soil too has its own cycle.

What happens to the solar energy that interacts with Earth and its atmosphere? To understand this and the global energy balance, we must examine the atmosphere through which the solar radiation passes.

7.4 Structure and composition of the atmosphere

Structure of the atmosphere

The atmosphere surrounding Earth is a gaseous envelope retained by gravity. It is most dense at the surface (90% of its mass is contained within the first 20 km and 99.9% of its mass within the first 50 km), and becomes thinner with increasing height, until at some 1000 km above us it merges seamlessly with interstellar space.

How does the thickness of the atmosphere compare with the radius of Earth?

The atmosphere is only a thin shell around the planet (but its influence on the conditions in which we live is enormous).

The atmosphere is divided into four distinct layers that are defined by their temperature characteristics. Each layer is called a sphere and the boundary between each layer is called a pause.

 Look at Figure 7.5. What happens to the density and the pressure as you rise through the atmosphere?

Density and pressure decrease.

The variation of temperature with height is much more complex.

The lowest layer, in which we live, is called the **troposphere**. Extending some 10 km above Earth's surface and containing 80% of the atmosphere's mass, it is a turbulent layer in which our weather is generated. The temperature generally decreases with increasing altitude, at a rate of 6.5°C km^{-1} up to a minimum of between –50°C and –55°C at the **tropopause**.

Above the tropopause, the **stratosphere** begins showing a gradual increase in temperature with altitude up to a maximum of 0°C at 50 km, at the **stratopause**. This maximum is the result of the absorption of the Sun's ultraviolet rays by **ozone**. Although only small amounts of ozone are present in this region, its presence is vital for the survival of life on

Figure 7.5
The vertical structure of the atmosphere

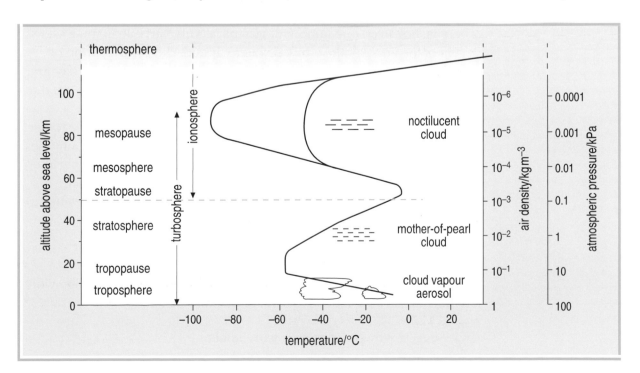

Earth, since it filters out much of the Sun's incoming biologically harmful ultraviolet radiation.

Above the stratosphere the temperature drops again through the region called the **mesosphere**. This is the coldest region in the atmosphere with a minimum of –90°C (183 K) at altitudes between 80 and 85 km, the **mesopause**.

Above the mesopause the temperature increases very rapidly with altitude. Daily variations in excess of 300°C may occur with a minimum near sunrise and a maximum about 2 p.m. This region is known as the **thermosphere** and at the top of it is the **thermopause**.

The physical reasons for these peculiar distributions of temperature in the atmosphere are related to the absorption of solar radiation. However, it is because ozone is a good absorber that a maximum temperature is found in the stratosphere while in the cold mesosphere the atmosphere is relatively transparent to solar radiation. The temperature reaches another maximum at the ground because of the absorption of solar energy at the surface.

Composition of the atmosphere

In the troposphere, stratosphere and mesosphere the major constituents of the atmosphere, molecular nitrogen and oxygen, are present in the proportion of approximately 80% to 20%, respectively.

Within the thermosphere, gas concentrations are extremely low and at altitudes above 500 km some of the gas molecules are able to escape the gravitational pull of Earth and drift into space. Thus, the atmosphere's chemical composition changes with altitude.

There is, however, one important gas that is very variable in the lower layers of the atmosphere – this is water vapour. The condensation of water vapour in the troposphere forms the clouds we see every day, but occasionally clouds can be observed in two higher levels. These are the 'mother of pearl' clouds, so-called because of their rainbow-like appearance. These appear at over 27 km above the ground in the lower stratosphere and consist of frozen water droplets. At still higher altitudes 'noctilucent' clouds can be seen at between 80 and 100 km. Visible after sunset while still illuminated by the setting Sun, they consist of ice crystals, probably formed around the dust remnants of meteorites burnt up as they entered Earth's gravitational field.

Rising through the atmosphere

As we saw in Figure 7.5, pressure, density and temperature change with altitude. Let us now look at this in a little more detail.

 Suggest why pressure falls with height.

The higher we go, the less weight of air there is pressing from above.

What would happen to a balloon as it rises through the atmosphere?

As the balloon rises it expands, because the external pressure decreases with height. It will eventually burst.

In fact, the pressure decreases exponentially, and the relationship between pressure and height is given by:

$$P = P_0 e^{-1.14 \times 10^{-4} b}$$

where P is the pressure at a height of b metres above Earth's surface and P_0 is the atmospheric pressure at Earth's surface (i.e. when $b = 0$)

Q4   Atmospheric pressure at Earth's surface is 1.01×10^5 Pa. What is the pressure at a height of 50 km, i.e. in the stratosphere. ◆

Q5   At what height is the pressure halved? ◆

The lapse rate

We have seen that pressure decreases as we travel upwards through the atmosphere. So what happens to temperature as we travel upwards through the troposphere? If you ever go walking in the hills, you may have noticed that the higher you climb, the cooler it becomes – this provides a clue. To keep things simple, we can consider the temperature change of a parcel of air, of unit mass, as it rises through the troposphere. As the parcel of air rises, its volume changes because of the pressure changes, while its mass remains constant. Thus, the volume can be expressed in terms of its density, $V \propto 1/\rho$. This situation is another example of the **first law of thermodynamics** (which you met in Section 4.3)

$$\Delta U = Q + W$$

where ΔU is the change of the **internal energy** of the air parcel, Q the thermal energy transferred to or from the air parcel and W the work done on or by the air parcel (each taking positive or negative values as appropriate). Using this law and the ideal gas equation ($PV = nRT$) it is possible to calculate the rate of change of temperature of the air parcel as it rises through the troposphere, doing work as it expands. The rate at which temperature falls with increasing height is called the **lapse rate**. It has been found that in the troposphere the lapse rate is about 1°C per 100 m.

A mountain is 2840 m high. Assuming a lapse rate of 1°C per 100 m, what is the temperature at the summit, given that the sea-level temperature is 20°C?

A lapse rate of 1°C in every 100 m means that temperature falls by 1°C for each 100 m increase in height, so at the top of a mountain 2840 m high, the temperature must be 28.4°C lower than the temperature at sea level. This means the temperature at the summit is −8.4°C.

7.5 Enhanced greenhouse effect (EGHE)

You are probably aware of the widespread concern about **global warming**. We would now like you to read the article 'The greenhouse effect' from the journal *New Scientist* (no. 92, 6 July 1996) which we have reproduced on pages 147–51, and then answer Questions 6–14 below. (When the greenhouse effect is increased by artificial causes, such as the burning of fossil fuels or the release of CFCs, it is called the **enhanced greenhouse effect**.)

Q6 Why, although the Earth and the Moon are roughly equidistant from the Sun, is the mean Earth temperature 15°C while the mean Moon temperature is −18°C? ◆

Q7 How does the Earth's greenhouse process differ from that of a glass greenhouse? ◆

Q8 Is the greenhouse effect a good thing or a bad thing? Why? ◆

Q9 What other gases are implicated in the greenhouse effect? Quantify their effect compared with CO_2. ◆

Q10 How are the computer models and predictions tested? ◆

Q11 Which is the most important artificial source of atmospheric CO_2? ◆

Q12 Substantiate the statement: 1 t of carbon, when burnt produces about 4 t of CO_2. ◆

Q13 Look at Figure 7.10 in the article. Compare the range of variations in the local mean temperature since 1850 with the 1850 value. ◆

Q14 Estimate from Figure 7.8 the percentage increase in atmospheric carbon dioxide since 1850. ◆

Life on Earth depends on it. But the greenhouse effect, fuelled by rising CO_2 levels, has also boosted global temperatures alarmingly. Computer models predict vast climatic changes. The heat is still on ...

THE GREENHOUSE EFFECT

John and Mary Gribbin

We on Earth are essentially the same distance from the Sun as is the Moon. Both our planet and the Moon receive the same amount of heat, averaged over the year, per square metre of their surface. Yet the Earth's average surface temperature is 15°C, while the Moon's is 18°C. This difference – a crucial one, as we shall see – is all down to the fact that the Earth has an atmosphere which, rather like a blanket, traps heat that would otherwise escape into space.

The warming of the surface that results is called the greenhouse effect. Often cited solely as the culprit in climate change, the greenhouse effect is in fact a good thing, keeping our planet comfortably warm and suitable for life as we know it. Remarkably, it is minor components of the atmosphere, notably carbon dioxide (CO_2) and water vapour that are responsible for this vital task.

Small amounts of these gases, known as greenhouse gases, have a big effect on temperature at the Earth's surface, and because of this the scientific community is concerned that human activity, and particularly adding more CO_2 to the atmosphere by burning fossil fuel, may be upsetting the natural balance. Greenhouse gases added in this way are known as 'anthropogenic', and are small in volume when compared with the bulk of the atmosphere, but large compared with the amount of natural greenhouse gases present before the start of the Industrial Revolution.

Although it is called the greenhouse effect, the process does not, in fact, involve trapping heat in the same way that a glass greenhouse does. The important feature of a greenhouse is that when the air inside it warms up, it cannot escape by convection. So the way to regulate the temperature inside a greenhouse is to open or close ventilators in its roof.

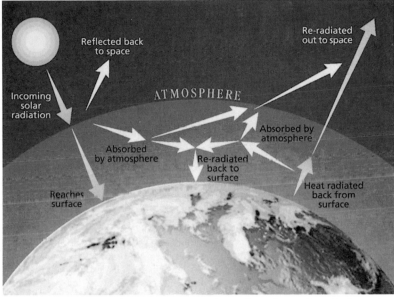

Figure 7.6   Some of the energy radiated at infrared wavelengths from the ground is absorbed and re-radiated downwards by the atmosphere – the greenhouse effect

The Earth's greenhouse effect operates in a different way. The Sun's energy radiates mainly in the visible part of the spectrum; this is why the radiation is visible as sunlight, our eyes have evolved to make use of what is available. This radiation, with wavelengths that range from 0.4 to 0.7 micrometres, passes through the Earth's atmosphere essentially unaltered, apart from a fraction reflected back into space. Even longer wavelengths, in the near infrared part of the spectrum, get through the air to warm the surface of the Earth [Figure 7.6].

Energy from the Sun

Trapping the heat

The Sun's surface temperature determines the nature of its radiation, and in particular where in the spectrum its energy output peaks. Essentially, the Sun radiates energy as a so-called black body – that is, with very little radiation at the long and short wavelengths and a peak of intensity somewhere in-between. The radiation that the Sun produces in the visible spectrum corresponds to a

temperature of just under 6000 K [Figure 7.7].

Warmth from the Sun heats the surface of the Earth, which radiates energy in its turn. In equilibrium, the Earth radiates back into space exactly the same amount of energy that it receives from the Sun, but at a much lower temperature – about 15°C. The black body spectrum corresponding to this temperature has a peak not in the visible waveband but in the infrared, chiefly in the range from 4 to 100 micrometres.

Some of this outgoing radiation from the Earth's surface is trapped in the atmosphere, close to the ground. Water vapour strongly absorbs radiation with wavelengths ranging from 4 to 7 micrometres, and CO_2 absorbs in the range from 13 to 19 micrometres. There is, however, a 'window' between 7 and 13 micrometres through which more than 70% of the radiation from the Earth's surface eventually escapes into space.

The trapped radiation warms the lower part of the Earth's atmosphere, the troposphere. In turn, this warmed air then radiates energy – largely in the infrared – in all directions. Some of this radiation works its way upward and out from the highest part of the atmosphere, but some finds its way back down to the Earth's surface, keeping it hotter than it would otherwise be. This is the greenhouse effect.

Because the temperature of the troposphere decreases the higher you go, the net effect is that each layer absorbs energy radiated from below, at warmer levels, and passes it upward, ultimately to escape into space. The overall effect is that less infrared radiation is lost, so the surface, and each intermediate layer, warms up until an equilibrium of absorption and radiation is restored.

The human factor
Searching for sinks

As we have noted, human activity, by increasing the amount of CO_2 in the atmosphere, adds to the natural greenhouse effect. Other anthropogenic greenhouse gases add to the effect by absorbing radiation in the window from 7 to 13 micrometres, which used to escape freely into space.

The system is, however, slightly more complicated than this. When the world warms a little because of an increase in the atmospheric concentration of CO_2 more water evaporates from the ocean and enters the atmosphere. This added water vapour itself contributes to the greenhouse effect, increasing the temperature by another small increment. The water vapour in fact makes a bigger contribution to the resultant warming than the CO_2 that initially caused the rise in temperature. But the natural state still tends towards equilibrium – provided the concentration of CO_2 stays the same – and all these **feedbacks** are allowed for in computer models of global warming. These models – discussed in detail below – are simplified computer representations of the global climate. Measurements of temperature and other data are entered and processed to help predict how the climatic system will behave over time.

Long before computers came onto the scene, however, scientists knew about the greenhouse effect. As early as 1827, the French polymath Jean-Baptiste Fourier suggested the existence of an effect keeping the Earth warmer than it would otherwise be, and was the first person to make the analogy – incorrect, as we have seen – with the action of panes of glass in a greenhouse. John Tyndall, an Irish scientist, published a

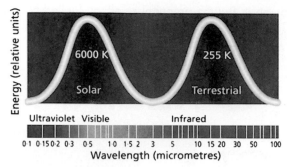

paper in the *Philosophical Magazine* in 1863 about the effect of water vapour as a greenhouse gas. In the 1890s, the Swedish scientist Svante Arrhenius and an American P. C. Chamberlain, both considered the problems that might be caused by a build-up of CO_2 in the air. They realized that the ongoing combustion of coal, the main fossil fuel of the time, could lead to global warming.

In the early part of the 20th century, average surface air temperatures did increase slightly, rising by about 0.25°C between 1880 and 1940. In the years following the US dustbowl of the 1930s, some scientists suggested that this was a sign of the anthropogenic greenhouse effect at work. But between 1940 and 1970 there was a world-wide cooling of 0.2°C, and the possibility of the global temperature rising as the result of the anthropogenic greenhouse effect was not a major subject of scientific research. Then, new measurements of the amount of CO_2 in the atmosphere,

Figure 7.7
The same amount of energy received from the Sun is radiated back into space, but at longer wavelengths

which began to show a significant increase, stimulated a wave of scientific activity in the 1970s. It was forecast that the pre-industrial concentration of CO_2 would double, causing the world to warm by about 2°C.

There is now no doubt that since the 19th century the amount of CO_2 and other anthropogenic greenhouse gases in the atmosphere has increased dramatically, and the average temperature of the world has also increased, if rather erratically. Questions remain about how much of the global warming can be blamed on the build-up of anthropogenic greenhouse gases, and how rapidly the world is likely to warm in the 21st century if – as seems inevitable – this build-up continues. The best figures currently available come from the 1996 report of the Intergovernmental Panel on Climate Change (IPCC), the independent scientific advisory body of the Climate Change Convention signed at Rio (see Box 1). The IPCC projects a most likely

---

1   The IPCC and the Climate Change Convention

Spurred on by concern over new measurements of carbon dioxide in the atmosphere, in 1988 the World Meteorological Organization and the United Nations Environment Programme began a global initiative to combat the problem – the Intergovernmental Panel on Climate Change (IPCC). The IPCC assesses research and policy options on climate change and reports on the risks of global warming. Its scientific working group alone draws on contributions from hundreds of researchers.

In 1990, the IPCC issued a report that shook the world, claiming that only strong measures to halt rising greenhouse gas emissions would prevent a dangerous rise in global warming. (The latest figures from the IPCC study group, some of which are used in this Inside Science, were published in June 1996.) The fruit of the IPCC's labour – the Climate Change Convention – was finally signed in 1992 at the Earth Summit in Rio, and ratified in 1993. The convention's aim is to stabilise greenhouse gases in the atmosphere at 1990 levels by the year 2000.

Are we getting any closer to making this happen? Many of the convention's signatories have dragged their feet over reducing emissions by the target date. And doubts have dogged the science behind the IPCC's reports: issues such as how far sea level will rise have generated fierce debate. But however embroiled in political and economic battles it becomes, the phenomenon of global warming itself marches on.

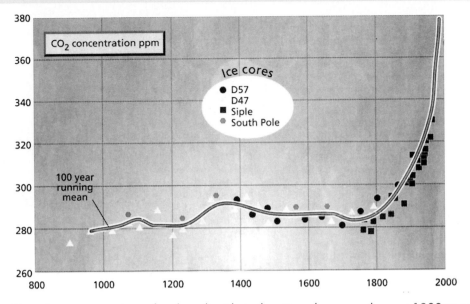

Figure 7.8   Changing concentrations of carbon dioxide in the atmosphere over the past 1000 years. The measurements are taken from four Antarctic ice cores and are combined with those from Mauna Loa, Hawaii. Note the rapid increase since about 1850 (Source: IPCC [Intergovernmental Panel on Climate Change])

warming of 2°C by the year 2100, with a corresponding rise in sea level of just under 0.5 metres. But just how these changes would alter rainfall and other weather patterns is as yet far from clear.

Researchers had begun to take accurate measurements of the amount of CO_2 in the air at Mauna Loa, Hawaii, and at the South Pole during the International Geophysical Year, 1957–58. These measurements are an important guide because they are taken far away from any major sources of industrial pollution, and represent the 'well-mixed' state of the atmosphere. They show a clear seasonal rhythm, associated with changes in the activity of vegetation over the land masses of the Northern Hemisphere. (The Earth's vegetation 'breathes' CO_2 in and out over an annual cycle, and the effect is dominated by the Northern Hemisphere because there is more land there.) By the 1970s, however, it became clear that this annual cycle was superimposed on a rising trend of global mean CO_2 concentration. This has now been borne out by studies of bubbles of old air trapped in the ice in Antarctica [Figure 7.8].

A burning issue

Gases on the rise

In 1957, the concentration of CO_2 in the atmosphere was 315 parts per million (ppm). It is now 360 ppm, that is, 0.036 per cent. Before the Industrial Revolution, the CO_2 concentration was below about 280 ppm. Most of the extra carbon required to make the CO_2 has

come from burning coal and other fossil fuel; while part of the increase may be due to the destruction of tropical forests. When 1 tonne of carbon is burnt, say in the form of coal, it produces about 4 tonnes of CO_2, as each carbon atom combines with two oxygen atoms from the air. In the 1980s, some 5 gigatonnes (5 billion tonnes, or 5 Gt) of carbon were being burnt in the form of fossil fuel each year, so the annual input of CO_2 to the atmosphere from this source was about 20 Gt.

The observed increase in the CO_2 content of the atmosphere, however, corresponds to just under half the amount of CO_2 human activities produce each year. Roughly half of the CO_2 we produce is absorbed by what are known as natural sink or sinks. Vegetation – including not just forests but also the **biomass** of the soil and the sea, both of which are dominated by micro-organisms – is a vital sink, growing more vigorously in an atmosphere enriched with CO_2. Some of the CO_2 may also dissolve in the oceans. One potential cause for concern is the possibility that whatever the natural sinks are, they may one day 'fill up' and stop absorbing CO_2. If this happened, the rate at which CO_2 is building up in the atmosphere could double.

Between 1850 and 1950, roughly 60 Gt of carbon were burnt, again chiefly as coal. The same amount of carbon is now being burnt every decade. Researchers estimate from the known amount of fossil fuel burnt, that in the

middle of the 19th century the natural concentration of CO_2 in the atmosphere was about 270 ppm. This is confirmed by those measurements of the composition of air bubbles which have survived after being trapped in the polar ice sheets before industrialisation began.

Further studies of air bubbles in ice cores drilled from the Antarctic ice sheet show that this concentration has stayed roughly constant since the end of the most recent major ice age, for at least 10 000 years. So calculations of the likely effect of the build-up of CO_2 and other greenhouse gases in the atmosphere are usually reported in terms of the overall effect normalized to this background level of 270 ppm. Taking CO_2 alone, the increase in concentration above the background level is already 33%, and other gases, such as the chlorofluorocarbons (CFCs), are also contributing to the anthropogenic greenhouse effect. This is causing a significant upset to the natural system.

In addition to CO_2, gases which are being released by human activities, and which absorb infrared radiation in the range from 7 to 13 micrometres, include CFCs, methane, nitrous oxide and ozone. CFCs are better known as the chemicals responsible for depletion of the ozone layer in the stratosphere. They are also extremely efficient greenhouse gases: a single molecule of either of the two most common CFCs has the same greenhouse warming effect as 10 000 molecules of CO_2. The release of CFCs may now have passed its peak, because of concern about ozone depletion; but these substances linger for a long time in the atmosphere and will continue to contribute to the greenhouse effect throughout the 21st century.

Methane has a very low atmospheric concentration of just under 2 ppm, but this is increasing at a rate of about 1.2% a year. The biological activity of bacteria in paddy fields is probably to blame, along with the release of natural gas from commercial oil and gas fields. Nitrous oxide, released by the use of nitrogen-based fertilisers, now has an atmospheric concentration of just under 0.4 ppm. Ozone is also increasing in the troposphere as a result of human activities.

In 1985, Veerhabadrhan Ramanathan of the University of Chicago calculated the combined effect of all these greenhouse gases, plus CO_2, and projected the growth in concentration of the gases in the air forward into the 21st century. He concluded that by the year 2030, the minor contributions from the gases other than CO_2 would add up to as big an effect as the extra CO_2 in the air, and that the total effect (including CO_2) would be as if the natural concentration of CO_2 had doubled. At that time, computer models suggested that this would imply a global warming of some 3°C above the level of the mid-19th century [Figure 7.9].

Of this projected 3°C rise in temperature, about 0.5°C has already happened [Figure 7.10], and although natural fluctuations in climate may have caused some of this warming, the actual rise in temperature since the 19th century is in line with computer models

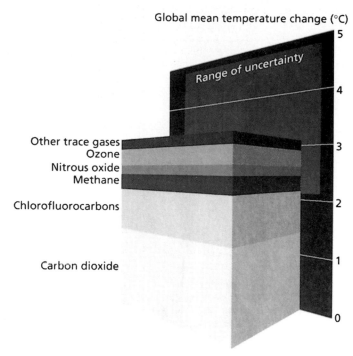

Figure 7.9   The likely overall warming of the world caused by the build-up of greenhouse gases released as a result of human activities between 1980 and 2030, including allowance for feedback effect (Source: V. Ramanathan and colleagues)

of the anthropogenic greenhouse effect expected from the build-up of CO_2 and other gases over that period. In the context of climatic records, the 1980s was the warmest decade, with seven of the eight warmest years up to 1990 the warmest year to date. To put this into perspective, the coldest years of the 1980s were warmer than the warmest years of the 1880s.

This warming trend was interrupted after 1990, but in a way that itself

showed how accurate the computer models which describe global warming are. The trigger for the interruption was Mount Pinatubo, a volcano in the Philippines, which erupted in June 1991 and threw an enormous amount of debris into the stratosphere. This material spread around the globe partially shielding the surface of the Earth from incoming solar energy. The same computer models used in calculations of the greenhouse effect

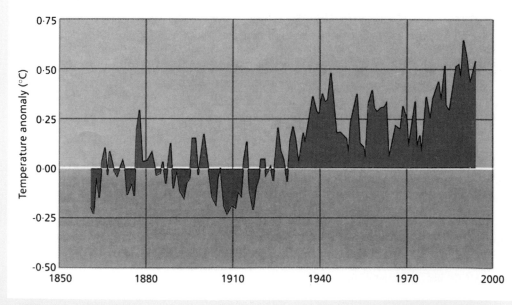

Figure 7.10 Observed changes in mean global temperature from 1861 to 1994 (Source: IPCC [Intergovernmental Panel on Climate Change])

predicted that in the short term, the debris would cool the Earth's atmosphere dramatically, temporarily returning average temperatures to the level of a century ago. This predicted cooling duly occurred over the following two years.

The models also predicted that as the volcanic debris cleared from the atmosphere in 1992 and 1993, average temperatures would swiftly return first to the level of the 1980s, and then, by the middle of the 1990s, to the slightly higher levels that would be expected with the ongoing build-up of greenhouse gases. Data for 1994 and 1995 show that these predictions were fully borne out, with 1995 itself failing by a hair's breadth to be the warmest year on record – within the limits of statistical uncertainty, it equalled the record set in 1990.

Mount Pinatubo was not the only recent factor in global cooling. Humans play a part, too; and since the mid-1980s, the biggest improvement in computer models of global climate is that they now take account of this. Burning fossil fuel releases not just CO_2 but also particulate matter known as aerosol, which, like volcanic debris, blocks out some of the incoming solar energy. When both CO_2 and aerosol are allowed for, the computer simulations mimic the actual pattern of climate changes in the 20th century very closely.

The new models were very useful in solving the puzzle of why northwestern Europe failed to warm as quickly as earlier models had predicted. Since it is not produced explosively, like volcanic debris, aerosol tends not to travel far from its source; so anthropogenic aerosol does not penetrate into the stratosphere and spread right around the world as CO_2 does. With aerosol so abundant over industrialised Europe, it was only with the advent of clean air legislation after

2 Rising sea levels and melting ice

The other immediate effect of an increase in global mean temperatures is a rise in sea level. This is already happening. Sea level has risen by about 15 centimetres during the 20th century, and the rise is very much in line with the rise in temperature that has occurred over the same interval. Most of this rise can be explained simply in terms of the thermal expansion of sea water.

Only a little extra water has been added to the sea, from melting glaciers on mountains at low latitudes. Paradoxical though it may seem, at present the polar ice caps may be increasing in size. This is because more moisture is evaporating at low latitudes, and falling as snow near the poles, where it is still cold. A global warming of about 2°C, possible within 40 years, will increase sea level by a further 30 centimetres. But one 'scare story' associated with the greenhouse effect is dismissed by the experts. This is the fear that the entire West Antarctic ice sheet might collapse, sliding into the ocean and raising sea level world-wide. Some calculations do suggest that once the world warms by about 4°C (which could happen within the next hundred years) the ice sheet might 'collapse'.

But what glaciologists mean by a collapse is still a slow process by everyday standards – it would take several hundred years for all the West Antarctic ice to slide into the sea, eventually raising sea levels by 5 metres or more, but only at a rate of 1 or 2 centimetres a year. There would be ample time to walk out of harm's way, although the impact on coastal cities and low-lying countries, such as Bangladesh and the Netherlands, would be catastrophic in the long term.

the Second World War that the aerosol cleared from over the region, bringing a rapid warming as it caught up with the rest of the world.

The best projections for the 21st century come from the IPCC report mentioned above. It predicts that global warming by the year 2100 will be in the range of 1°C to 3.5°C, with a 'best estimate' of 2°C. Sea level (see Box 2) will rise as a result, both because of melting glaciers and ice caps and because, as the top layer of ocean warms, it will expand. The predicted rise by the year 2100 is between 15 centimetres and 90 centimetres, with a best estimate of 48 centimetres. This will place 9 million people at risk from flooding.

The 'best' warming rate predicted by the IPCC study is 0.2°C per decade. To put that in perspective, the predicted rate of change is about 50 times faster than the warming which brought an end to the last major ice age which, up to that point, was itself the largest sustained natural change in climate for the past 100 000 years.

FURTHER READING

Global Warming, by John Houghton (Lion); *Climate Change* and *Climate Change 1996*, IPCC (CUP); *Watching the Weather*, by John and Mary Gribbin (Constable).

John Gribbin is a visiting fellow in astronomy at the University of Sussex.

Mary Gribbin teaches at a secondary school.

All graphics are by Nigel Hawtin.

(*New Scientist*, no. 92, 6 July 1996)

Feedback systems

 Suppose that a small rise in temperature caused a growth in desert areas. Sand is more reflective than vegetation – it has a higher albedo. What effect would this have on incoming radiation when it strikes the ground?

More will be reflected than before.

 What will happen to the temperature of the Earth?

It could fall.

 What should happen to the desert region?

It should decrease in size.

 What if it retreats a lot?

More energy would reach Earth, so the process could repeat and an oscillation set in.

Such a process is called feedback: the output, in this case size of desert, affects the input, the net solar energy input to Earth – an increase in the size of the desert causes a reduction in the input and vice versa. This is called **negative feedback**.

In the same way, an increase in temperature could reduce the areas covered by snow and ice, so lowering the albedo and causing more energy to be absorbed, resulting in a further rise in temperature. This is a **positive feedback** system.

 Given rising temperatures, humans tend to use more air-conditioning equipment, which when scrapped, or if faulty, leaks chlorofluorocarbons (CFCs) into the atmosphere and when in use consumes energy. Analyse the feedback system that may result.

More air-conditioning could lead to the release of more greenhouse gas and more enhanced greenhouse effect, which means higher temperatures and more demand for air-conditioning. However, more CFC leakage results in ozone depletion. Ozone is also a greenhouse gas, so this forms a negative feedback effect. More energy consumed in driving air-conditioners could emit more CO_2, enhancing the greenhouse effect further.

We really need to know the sizes of each effect to be sure whether the overall feedback is positive or negative.

The feedback systems implicated in the enhanced greenhouse effect are clearly diverse and complex. Global warming might lessen heating energy demand in some areas, but necessitate more cooling elsewhere, resulting in higher energy consumption. Paradoxically, reducing some pollutants could reduce cloud cover, which would lower the amount of radiation being reflected away from Earth in the first place. Models are still not sophisticated enough to accommodate all the parameters involved and they yield inconsistent results. Though in some ways related, the greenhouse effect must not be confused with the destruction of the ozone layer.

The fact that enormous amounts of energy are needed to warm the oceans means that the consequences of an increased (or decreased) greenhouse effect may take decades or even a century to reveal themselves (the CFCs that destroy ozone have an equally lingering effect). Several solutions to global warming are proposed:

- *Technical fixes.* For example, blasting dust into the upper atmosphere to increase albedo. Technical fixes are controversial and unproven, so they are not often used.

- *Mitigation.* For example, a programme of reforestation could be introduced so that the extra trees reabsorb excess CO_2. The countries in which rainforests exist (or used to) see the desire of the developed nations to restrict clearing as another example of their being restrained from enjoying the fruits of agricultural or industrial development. Nevertheless, at least one American utilityµôs promoting the planting of rainforests. The Applied Energy Services of Arlington, Virginia, paid for 52 million trees to be planted in Guatemala, to reverse the detrimental effect of greenhouse emissions from a new coal-fired power station in Connecticut.

- *Adaptation.* This means learning to cope with global warming and is the solution favoured by some economists. However, much heating and refrigeration plant and flood defences might be needed. This is a high-cost, risky and unguaranteed solution. Ironically, the sea defences needed to cope with rising water levels are often made with tropical hardwoods!

- *Preventative action.* This requires political treaties like those made at Rio to limit CFC or CO_2 emissions, for example, together with technological research and development of non-emitting devices.

In fact there is a simple (in principle) remedy to greenhouse gas emission, global warming and thermal pollution. All we need to do is to reduce fossil fuel consumption and replace it with solar energy. Merely 'borrowing' solar energy has no effect at all on radiation balance and global warming.

 What difficulty do you foresee with such a policy?

It would require a huge investment in solar technologies – this could take time, even if the will was there.

Energy companies also engage in this debate and so we have reproduced for you the chairman of Esso's approach to global climate change.

I believe that an approach is required that combines environmental, economic and social priorities, and that policies must recognise the scientific uncertainty surrounding global climate change and involve the developing countries as well.

In my view there is a need for a much more informed debate to take place before we plunge into adopting quick-fix policies that we may well regret later. Many scientists agree that we still have time to better understand global and regional climate systems.

However, this does not mean that I advocate standing still. There are a number of steps that the world can be taking now – all of which make sense in their own right, are cost-effective and will help to limit growth in greenhouse gas emissions. They include:

■ Encouraging increased efficiency in energy supply and demand by reducing government intervention and subsidies that artificially hold prices below real market levels or limit inter-fuel competition, and inhibit conservation.

■ Making it easier for best practice and innovation to enter the market and reduce future emissions by promoting free trade and open markets.

■ Persuading developing countries to accept direct foreign investment, which will bring with it the technology, management skills and expertise to help them improve energy efficiency and reduce emissions – thus avoiding the continued use of out-of-date technology.

■ Identifying and reducing barriers that prevent market penetration of potentially cost-effective technologies such as the use of combined heat and power projects.

■ Investing in ways to improve scientific, economic and technological understanding of climate change, its impacts and the economic and social effects of response options. Routine, long-term monitoring of climate, the climate process and major ecosystems is a key part of this.

■ Improving husbandry of the world's forests and woodlands to help the absorption of carbon dioxide – measures could include slowing deforestation and encouraging sound forest management practices.

■ Conducting research into future options for energy supply and end use, and the removal and storage of emissions of carbon dioxide.

(Keith Taylor, 'Climate change – a time for cool assessment not hot air', *ESSOVIEW*, Public Affairs Department, Esso UK plc, London, November 1996.)

Do you agree with his views? Which approach would you prioritize?

In Section 8 we shall explore how solar energy produces these alternative 'fuels'. To understand the mechanics of some of them, we need to look at our Earth sciences just a little more.

7.6 Motions in the atmosphere: the global circulation system

If we are to explain atmospheric motion we must understand the process of thermal convection. Most of the weather we experience occurs in the lowest layer of the atmosphere, i.e. the troposphere. Motion in the atmosphere, e.g. winds, may occur if there are pressure differences between one region of the atmosphere and its neighbours. Such pressure differences may be induced by uneven heating or cooling within the atmosphere.

 Given that water has a higher heat capacity than land, try to explain why winds blow from sea to land during the day and in the other direction at night.

The land (and the air above it) warms more quickly during the day and cools more quickly at night. Convection air currents will flow towards the land in the daytime and towards the sea at night.

We will now extend the concept of convection to Earth. The first model to describe larger-scale global convection was proposed by George Hadley in 1735. He noted that air nearer the Equator is warmer than that near the poles, because of the greater **solar flux** reaching the Equator. Tropical air should therefore rise vertically and, in the Northern Hemisphere, move northward while the colder polar air should move southward. As the tropical air moves north so it will lose energy by radiating energy before descending to replace the southward moving cold air. Similarly, the cold air will gain thermal energy from the ground (which is heated by solar radiation) and so rise in the equatorial regions.

Thus, a circulation system, capable of transporting thermal energy from the Equator to the poles, is established.

Hadley's model has at least two shortcomings as circulation turns out to be more complicated. First, the circulation system occurs not simply between Equator and poles, but within regions (called cells) bounded by the Equator (Hadley cells), the poles (polar cells) and the 30° and 60° latitudes (Ferrel cells) – see Figure 7.11 overleaf. Second, winds do not blow directly from high-pressure regions to low. The path the wind takes is distorted by the **Coriolis effect**, which arises from Earth's rotation.

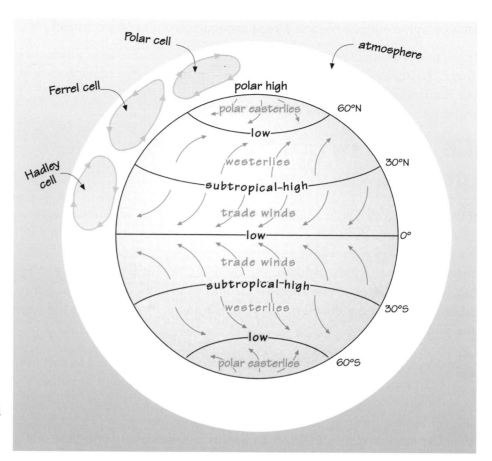

Figure 7.11
The Earth's wind and pressure distribution and circulation cells

7.7 Effects of the spinning Earth

The directions of the winds result from the interaction of the three convection cells in Figure 7.11 combined with the effects of a rotating Earth. Let us see why this happens. Earth rotates on its own axis once every 24 hours. We will treat the region around the North Pole as a rotating disc, as shown in Figure 7.12.

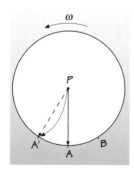

Figure 7.12
The Coriolis effect

An air parcel starts to move horizontally away from the pole, P, towards a point A. If no forces act on this air parcel, by Newton's laws it will follow a direct undeflected path to A. In fact, the air parcel does travel in a straight line but by the time it reaches the edge of the disc, A′ has rotated to A and A has rotated to B.

To an observer rotating with the Earth it will then look as if a deflectory force is acting on the parcel deflecting it away from A towards A′. This fictitious force is known as the **Coriolis force**.

Suppose a parcel of air of mass m moves outwards a distance r in time t. Its mean linear speed in this direction will be $v = r/t$. (If you have used the SLIPP unit *Physics in Space* you should know from Appendix 6.1 that angular velocity ω is related to actual velocity of an object by $v = r\omega$.) In this time the disc has rotated ωt and the point at which the parcel has arrived has moved a distance $s = r\omega t$ sideways, or the parcel appears to have been displaced a distance s in the opposite direction; that is, perpendicular to its original motion. Remember, $s = \frac{1}{2}at^2$.

Putting

$$r\omega t = \frac{1}{2}at^2$$

gives

$$a = \frac{2r\omega}{t}$$
$$= 2\omega v$$

and the fictitious force that moves it is equal to $2\omega v m$. Thus, to Earth-bound observers the wind appears to be steered increasingly to the right of the initial direction of movement in the Northern Hemisphere and to the left in the Southern Hemisphere, while the effect is absent over the Equator.

Such deflections may continue until the wind is blowing perpendicular to the original motion and so at right angles to the pressure gradient inducing it. It cannot then be deflected any further. At this stage a state of balance is achieved between the pressure and Coriolis forces that are equal but opposite.

So far we have considered separately the contribution that the atmosphere, the hydrosphere, and, in passing, the elements of the biosphere and the soil make to the climate of Earth. In reality, climate is generated by complex interactions between all four of these elements.

We are now in a position to summarize energy flows for the whole Earth; look at Figure 7.13 oveleaf.

About 30% of incoming solar energy, averaging for Earth as a whole, is reflected, by Earth's surface, upper atmosphere and cloud. Radiation that penetrates the atmosphere is selectively absorbed by the various atoms and molecules in the atmosphere (mainly water and carbon dioxide), and then re-radiated in all directions. This means that the amount of energy of the particular wavelength affected that is able to get through is much reduced. A secondary effect of this process is that the energy reaching Earth's surface does so not only from the direction of the Sun itself, but from all over the sky. This leads to the so-called diffuse component of the Sun's radiation, which, because clouds cover about half of Earth's surface at any one time, is not negligible. In Britain, diffuse radiation may contribute up to one half of our total influx of solar radiation or insolation.

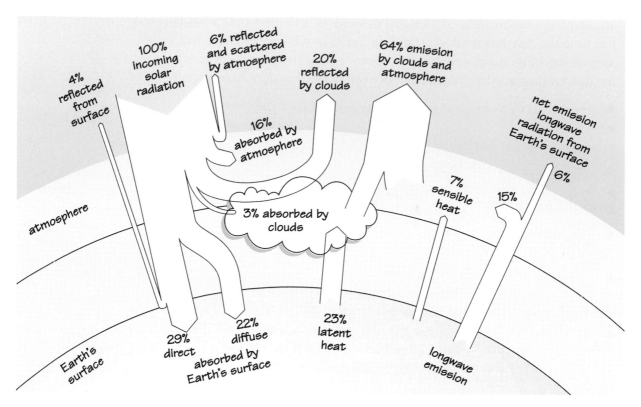

Figure 7.13 Mean energy balance for Earth–atmosphere–cloud system. (Two further small fluxes of energy arrive as tidal and geothermal energy; their contributions to the biosphere ultimately leave as longwave radiation. About 0.22% of incoming energy is transferred to winds (which in turn cause waves) and ocean currents; all of their energies ultimately depart as longwave radiation) (*Note:* The word 'net' refers to the fact that longwave radiation can 'cycle' between atmosphere and surface several times. The atmosphere is represented stylistically)

The atmosphere (including clouds) absorbs and stores solar energy – the differences in atmospheric pressure resulting from variations in energy stored give rise to the winds, which in turn cause waves on the sea. Solar energy is also absorbed by the land and the sea, causing evaporation leading to rain (and potentially, therefore, hydro power when it falls again) together with ocean currents driven by temperature differences. Only 0.22% of incoming solar energy manifests itself as wind, waves or ocean currents; nevertheless, the resource is large compared with the energy used by humans. Notice how all these phenomena are driven by *differences* in temperature or pressure.

 It should be clearer now which energy sources are truly renewable. Which are they?

Solar energy itself, wind, waves, some thermal energy in the oceans, hydroelectric power and biomass.

Achievements

After working through this section you should be able to:

- describe why water is a unique molecule
- describe the main features of the hydrologic cycle
- explain how clouds form
- explain the role of the biosphere and the soil in maintaining a radiation balance
- describe how thermal convection occurs in the atmosphere
- explain, in terms of specific heat capacity, why sea breezes occur during the day and land breezes at night
- describe the tricellular model of atmospheric circulation
- explain with the help of the Coriolis effect, how the spinning Earth creates the global wind patterns.

Glossary

Albedo The fraction of incident light reflected from a surface.

Biomass Living mass. In our present context it refers to living mass that may be used to produce fuel.

Biosphere Narrow zone between the lower atmosphere and the soil.

Coriolis effect The apparent spiralling effect (as seen by a stationary observer on Earth) of air currents above Earth due to the combination of convection currents and the turning of Earth.

Coriolis force An imaginary force that accounts for the Coriolis effect as observed from Earth.

Electric dipole Two opposite charges that are attached. Such a system will twist in an electric field.

Enhanced greenhouse effect The increased heating of the biosphere due to artificial causes, such as the increase of carbon dioxide from the burning of fossil fuels.

Feedback A process whereby all or part of the output of a system affects the input so that it modifies the output.

First law of thermodynamics The law of conservation of energy applied to heat transfer in gases. A positive change in the internal energy of a gas ΔU, is given by $\Delta U = Q + W$, where Q is the thermal energy transferred to the gas and W is the work done on the gas.

Global warming The increased warming of the biosphere due to the enhanced greenhouse effect.

Hydrologic cycle The cycle of evaporation and condensation of water on the global scale.

Hydrosphere The combination of oceans, rivers, water vapour and underground water, through which the hydrologic cycle takes place.

Internal energy Unit: joule (J); symbol U. The sum of the random kinetic and potential energies of molecules.

Lapse rate The rate of fall of a variable quantity such as temperature with height.

Mesopause The top of the mesosphere at about 85 km above Earth.

Mesosphere The region of the atmosphere above the stratosphere, 50–85 km from Earth, in which the temperature falls with height.

Negative feedback A process in which an increase in the output of a system causes a decrease in the input, and vice versa.

Ozone The gas O_3, which is produced by electrical discharge through air or oxygen or by the exposure of oxygen molecules to ultraviolet radiation.

Photosynthesis   The use of light energy by plants to power the chemical reactions involved in the manufacture of sugars from carbon dioxide and water.

Polar molecule   A molecule with a separation of charge leading to positive and negative regions or poles.

Positive feedback   A process in which an increase in the output of a system causes an increase in the input, which causes a further increase in the output.

Radiation balance   The situation when the temperature attained by a body leads to the emission and absorption of electromagnetic radiation being equal.

Saturated vapour   A concentrated vapour that exists in equilibrium with liquid of the same substance.

Solar flux   The rate of energy transmission per unit area of solar energy.

Stratopause   The top of the stratosphere 50–55 km above Earth's surface.

Stratosphere   The region of the atmosphere above the troposphere in which temperature increases with height because of absorption of ultraviolet radiation from the Sun.

Thermopause   The top of the thermosphere.

Thermosphere   The region of the atmosphere above the mesosphere where temperature increases rapidly with altitude.

Transpiration   Loss of water from the leaves of plants by evaporation.

Tropopause   The top of the troposphere at 9 km (poles) to 17 km (Equator) from Earth's surface.

Troposphere   The lowest part of the atmosphere in which temperature decreases uniformly with height. It extends from Earth's surface up to between 9 and 17 km.

Answers to Ready to Study test

R1

Density of concrete $= 2700 \, \text{kg} \, \text{m}^{-3}$

Volume of concrete $= 32.0 \, \text{m} \times 5.00 \, \text{m} \times 0.50 \, \text{m}$

$$= 80.0 \, \text{m}^3$$

Therefore

mass of concrete $=$ density $\times$ volume

$$= 2700 \, \text{kg} \, \text{m}^{-3} \times 80.0 \, \text{m}^3$$

$$= 2.16 \times 10^5 \, \text{kg}$$

thermal energy lost by concrete

$$= \text{mass} \times \text{specific heat capacity}$$
$$\times \text{temperature change}$$

$$= 2.16 \times 10^5 \, \text{kg} \times 850 \, \text{J} \, \text{kg}^{-1} \, \text{K}^{-1} \times 20 \, \text{K}$$

$$= 3.7 \times 10^9 \, \text{J} \, (\text{to two significant figures})$$

R2

If m is the mass of the wax and L is the specific latent heat of fusion of wax, then during solidification

thermal energy given out by wax

$$= mL$$

$$= 750 \, \text{kg} \times 1.4 \times 10^4 \, \text{J} \, \text{kg}^{-1}$$

$$= 1.1 \times 10^7 \, \text{J}$$

$$(\text{to two significant figures})$$

This is a type of latent heat, since its loss caused no temperature change in the wax.

When the wax cools from 32°C to 16°C

thermal energy lost by wax

$$= \text{mass}$$
$$\times \text{specific heat capacity}$$
$$\times \text{temperature change}$$
$$= 750 \,\text{kg} \times 110 \,\text{J} \,\text{kg}^{-1} \,\text{kg}^{-1} \times 16 \,\text{K}$$
$$= 1.3 \times 10^6 \,\text{J}$$
(to two significant figures)

This heat loss was in the form of **sensible heat**, i.e. it was accompanied by a fall in temperature.

Answers to questions in the text

Q1

Let the mass of steam condensed be m_s and the mass of the coffee be m_c.

Energy gained by coffee

$$= m_c \times c \times \text{temperature change}$$
$$= m_c \times 4.2 \times 10^3 \,\text{J} \,\text{kg}^{-1} \,\text{K}^{-1} \times 80 \,\text{K}$$
$$= 3.36 \times 10^5 \, m_c \,\text{J} \,\text{kg}^{-1}$$

Energy lost by steam $= m_s L$

where L is the latent heat of vaporization of water.

Assuming no energy losses

energy gained by coffee = energy lost by steam

$$m_c \times 3.36 \times 10^5 \,\text{J} \,\text{kg}^{-1} = m_s \times 2.3 \times 10^6 \,\text{J} \,\text{kg}^{-1}$$

so

$$\frac{m_s}{m_c} = \frac{3.36 \times 10^5 \,\text{J} \,\text{kg}^{-1}}{2.3 \times 10^6 \,\text{J} \,\text{kg}^{-1}}$$
$$= 0.15 \text{ (to two significant figures)}$$

So the steam increases the mass of the coffee by 0.15 of the original mass of coffee.

Q2

Assuming that the drink cools to 0°C, let the mass of the ice be m_i and the mass of drink be m_d.

Energy lost by drink

$$= m_d \times c \times \text{temperature drop}$$
$$= m_d \times 4.2 \times 10^3 \,\text{J} \,\text{kg}^{-1} \,\text{K}^{-1} \times 15 \,\text{K}$$
$$= 6.3 \times 10^4 \, m_d \,\text{J} \,\text{kg}^{-1}$$

Energy gained by melting ice $= m_i L$

where L is the latent heat of fusion of water.

Assuming no energy losses

energy lost by drink = energy gained by ice

$$6.3 \times 10^4 \, m_d \,\text{J} \,\text{kg}^{-1} = m_i \times 3.34 \times 10^5 \,\text{J} \,\text{kg}^{-1}$$

so

$$\frac{m_i}{m_d} = \frac{6.3 \times 10^4 \,\text{J} \,\text{kg}^{-1}}{3.34 \times 10^5 \,\text{J} \,\text{kg}^{-1}}$$
$$= 0.19 \text{ (to two significant figures)}$$

(i.e. approximately a fifth of the mass of drink, excluding ice, should be ice.)

Q3

(a)

$$m = \rho V$$
$$= \rho \frac{4}{3} \pi r^3$$

so

$$m_1 = 1000 \,\text{kg} \,\text{m}^{-3} \frac{4}{3} \pi \left(10 \times 10^{-6} \,\text{m}\right)^3$$
$$= 4.19 \times 10^{-12} \,\text{kg}$$
$$= 4.2 \times 10^{-12} \,\text{kg}$$
(to two significant figures)

(b)

$$m_2 = 50 \times 10^6 \times 4.19 \times 10^{-12} \, \text{kg}$$

$$= 2.1 \times 10^{-4} \, \text{kg (to two significant figures)}$$

So clouds don't have much mass!

Q4

$$P = 1.01 \times 10^5 \, \text{Pa} \times e^{-1.14 \times 10^{-4} \times 5 \times 10^4}$$

$$= 338 \, \text{Pa (to three significant figures)}$$

Q5

The pressure has halved when $\dfrac{P}{P_0} = 0.5$

so

$$0.5 = e^{-1.14 \times 10^{-4} h}$$

and

$$\ln 0.5 = -1.14 \times 10^{-4} h$$

therefore

$$h = \frac{-0.693}{-1.14 \times 10^{-4}}$$

$$= 6.08 \times 10^4 \text{ (to three significant figures)}$$

i.e. the top of a very high mountain.

Q6

Earth's higher temperature is due to the insulating effect of its atmosphere.

Q7

The warm air inside a greenhouse is trapped and cannot escape in a convection current.

Radiation from the Sun can pass through the atmosphere to reach the surface of Earth and warm it. Radiation with wavelengths in the visible part of the spectrum and the near infrared is trapped in the atmosphere and absorbed by water vapour and carbon dioxide in the atmosphere. Some of this energy is re-radiated causing a warming of the atmosphere.

Q8

Life on Earth has evolved slowly in such a way that it has adapted to the (in the long term, stable) atmospheric temperature created by the natural greenhouse effect. Any relatively rapid change in atmospheric temperature could have disastrous consequences for life on Earth. So the natural greenhouse effect is good, but the enhanced greenhouse effect is not.

Q9

Other gases implicated in the greenhouse effect are:

(a) CFCs (chlorofluorocarbons). At the most extreme one molecule can have the same effect as 10 000 molecules of CO_2.

(b) Methane (2 ppm in the atmosphere, but rising).

(c) Nitrous oxide (0.4 ppm in the atmosphere).

(d) Ozone.

(e) Water vapour.

Veerhabadrhan Ramanathan predicts that a combined effect of these gases plus the increase in CO_2 concentration will be equivalent to the natural CO_2 concentration doubling by 2030.

Q10

The predictions and models are tested by examining their accuracy when actual data becomes available.

Q11

The burning of fossil fuels.

Q12

The formula for the burning of carbon is

$$C + O_2 \rightarrow CO_2$$

The atomic mass of carbon is 12 g mol^{-1} and that of oxygen is 16 g mol^{-1}. So 1 mol of

CO_2 has mass $(12 + 16 + 16)$ g $= 44$ g, while 1 mol of carbon has a mass of 12 g. As 44 g is approximately 4 times 12 g, 1 t of carbon, when burnt, produces about 4 t of CO_2

Q13

Until 1940, the mean temperature was within the range from 0.25°C below to about 0.30°C above the 1850 value. Since 1940, the mean temperature change has consisted of a rise of between about 0.2°C and 0.7°C compared with the 1850 value.

Q14

From Figure 7.8, initial concentration in 1850 was 295 ppm and present concentration is approximately 370 ppm, so

$$% \text{ increase} = \frac{370 - 295}{295} \times 100\%$$
$$= 25.4\%$$
$$= 25\% \text{ (to two significant figures)}$$

8

In this section, we will see that there are several Sun-derived alternatives to fossil fuels. From Section 7 you have learnt that the rate of fossil fuel creation must be a very small fraction of 40×10^{12} W, itself a small fraction of the solar energy arriving at Earth of 171×10^{15} W. In other words, the rate of fossil fuel creation is much lower than the rate at which we use energy, which now exceeds 10.9×10^{12} W for the world. We may therefore treat fossil fuel reserves as a fixed, non-replaceable resource – such resources are known as **capital sources**. Solar energy, wind, wave, ocean current, hydroelectric power, biomass and all other solar-derived energies are **income sources** – they are fairly continuous and inexhaustible (although it is possible that biomass could be used up quicker than it is produced). And, if we simply borrow solar power or its derivatives during the thermal decay process and employ them usefully, we do not alter the equilibrium temperature or cause pollution.

READY TO STUDY TEST

Before you begin this section you should be able to:

- work out, confirm or derive using Ohm's law: internal resistance and loads, power delivered to a load, efficiency, and energy delivery by a battery
- define change in thermal energy = $mc\,\Delta\theta$ or ml
- state Newton's second law and the equations of constant acceleration
- define 'work done' and 'power'
- define the amount of energy in a photon
- use the formulas for kinetic energy and potential energy.

QUESTIONS

R1 A cyclist increases her speed uniformly from 3.0 m s^{-1} to 9.0 m s^{-1} in 12 s. She and her cycle have a combined mass of 75 kg.

(a) What resultant force acts on the cycle?

(b) If the mean frictional force on the cycle is 15 N, what tractive force does the cyclist supply at the rear wheel (i.e. the force acting along the road surface)?

(c) How far does the cycle travel during the acceleration?

(d) What is the work done by the cyclist?

(e) What is the mean power output of the cyclist?

R2 When she's arrived, the cyclist's friend thinks it would be very funny to hose her down to cool her off. The hose delivers 2.0 litre s^{-1} through a nozzle of cross-sectional area 2.0×10^{-4} m^2 and the density, ρ, for water is 1000 kg m^{-3}. If the water is stopped entirely on impact, what force does she experience?

R3 A 4.5 V battery delivers 0.40 A for 5.0 h and costs £2.70. (a) What is the cost of this electricity per kW h and (b) how much charge flows in this time?

R4 Determine the energy of photons of wavelengths 483 nm and 10 μm.

8.1 Solar energy technology

The Sun's energy may be transferred into thermal energy or electrical energy (or both, using a hybrid system). As a source of 'clean' (non-polluting) energy the Sun cannot be bettered. In France, concentrated solar power is used for high-temperature (4000°C) research. In Greece, on the island of Patmos, 38 000 litres of water per day is purified using solar power. But for much of the world, particularly the UK, one problem with solar power is that it is variable. While, over the long term, we know fairly accurately how much solar energy will arrive at any one place, supply is *unpredictable* for a specific time. Over a short time span, then, solar power is **unfirm**.

However, the problem of variability can be solved by over-designing the capacity of the system so that periods of low energy supply can still meet demand or by including a back-up system for winter and cloudy summer days. Alternatively, some means of storage can be provided to overcome periods of deficit: short-term for cloudy summer days or long-term for the winter.

Solar furnace used for high-temperature research at Odeilo, France

Thermal flat solar panel collectors

Thermal flat solar panel collectors often take the form of a darkened plate connected to a water pipe with an inlet and outlet connection; they are insulated underneath and covered with glass. We will analyse one like this in a simplified way.

Energy enters such a panel in the form of solar radiation and thermal energy in the water input. Energy leaves the panel as thermal energy lost to the surroundings and thermal energy in the water outlet.

Let's assume that the solar radiation falling on a solar panel is 600 W m^{-2}, and the energy lost to the surroundings occurs only through the glass (at a rate of 5.0 W m^{-2} K^{-1}, that is 5.0 W from each square metre for every degree above the temperature of the surroundings). Figure 8.1 shows a solar water heating system.

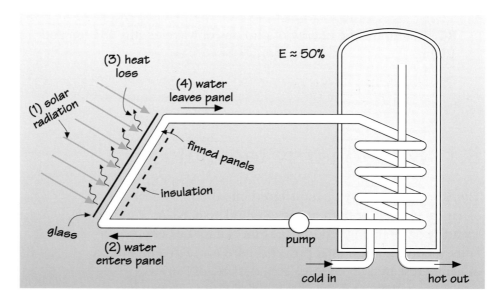

Figure 8.1 Solar hot water system. Care must be taken to set the level of each part so that convection currents do not cool the tank. If the tank is above the panel, there is no need for a pump. Antifreeze has to be added to the circulating water if the panel is to be used in frosty conditions

 If water enters the tank with temperature θ_{in} and leaves with temperature θ_{out}, how is thermal energy supply rate, Q, related to mass flow rate m'?

Rate of thermal energy supply, $Q = m'c(\theta_{out} - \theta_{in})$.

 Write an expression in words relating the rates of energy flow into and out of the panel, then express it as an equation. Take the panel area as A and assume that the temperature of the pipes and the collector surface is the mean of θ_{in} and θ_{out} and the surrounding temperature is θ_{sur}.

Rate of solar heat supply equals rate of thermal energy increase in water plus rate of heat loss from panel

$$600\,\text{W}\,\text{m}^{-2}A = m'c(\theta_{out} - \theta_{in}) + A \times 5.0\,\text{W}\,\text{m}^{-2}\,\text{K}^{-1}\left(\frac{\theta_{out} + \theta_{in}}{2} - \theta_{sur}\right)$$

$$(8.1)$$

How would you define the efficiency, ε, of the panel?

$$\varepsilon = \frac{\text{energy supplied by panel to water}}{\text{energy supplied by Sun to panel}}$$

$$= \frac{m'c(\theta_{out} - \theta_{in})}{600\,\text{W m}^{-2}A}$$

(8.2)

Now, dividing both sides of Equation (8.1) by 600 W m^{-2} A gives

$$1 = \frac{m'c(\theta_{out} - \theta_{in})}{600\,\text{W m}^{-2}A} + \frac{A \times 5.0\,\text{W m}^{-2}\text{K}^{-1}\left(\dfrac{\theta_{out} + \theta_{in}}{2} - \theta_{sur}\right)}{600\,\text{W m}^{-2}A}$$

(8.3)

Since (from Equation 8.2)

$$\varepsilon = \frac{m'c(\theta_{out} - \theta_{in})}{600\,\text{W m}^{-2}A}$$

Equation (8.3) becomes

$$1 = \varepsilon + \frac{5.0\left(\dfrac{\theta_{out} + \theta_{in}}{2} - \theta_{sur}\right)\text{K}^{-1}}{600}$$

(8.4)

Therefore

$$\varepsilon = 1 - \frac{5.0\left(\dfrac{\theta_{out} + \theta_{in}}{2} - \theta_{sur}\right)\text{K}^{-1}}{600}$$

(8.5)

Q1 Use the values $c = 4200$ J kg^{-1} °C^{-1}, $A = 1.0$ m^2, $\theta_{in} = 10$°C, $\theta_{sur} = 15$°C to answer the following. (*Note:* As we are dealing with temperature differences here you do not need to convert from °C to K.)

(a) Simplify Equation (8.5) and plot ε against θ_{out} for θ_{out} between 10°C and 100°C. Include space for ε from 0 to 1 on your graph. What does your graph show?

(b) What is the efficiency at 40°C, 70°C and 100°C output?

(c) Returning to Equation (8.2), what water flow rates could be sustained at 70°C output? ◆

Solar power and the production of electricity

Solar power driving turbines

In flat-plate collection, devices similar to roof-top domestic collectors vaporize a working fluid (possibly water under reduced pressure), which powers turbines, which, in turn, drive generators as in a normal thermal power station – the collectors do not move. Temperatures are low and so diffuse radiation may be collected and heat losses are reduced – nevertheless, efficiency only approaches 5% because of the number of energy transfers (all with 'losses') taking place. The same technology is used in Sun-tracking **concentrating collectors**. These are more efficient overall, approaching the efficiency of a typical present-day thermal power station, but they are more complicated and therefore more costly. Such systems are likely to be centralized and large.

Biomass

The Sun's rays may, of course, be used to grow plants for use as an energy supply. The energy from this biomass may be released directly by burning, or the biogas that is produced when the biomass decays may be used. As we mentioned in Section 4.6, Brazil uses ethanol produced by the fermentation of sugar cane instead of (or in addition to) petroleum in some cars. Sun-warmed algae may feed on waste to produce a fuel – the efficiencies of such systems might approach only 3%, but they would also consume atmospheric CO_2 while the fuels are growing.

Energy from sugar cane

Why is this an advantage?

As you learnt in Section 7, atmospheric CO_2 enhances the greenhouse effect and contributes to global warming.

Photovoltaic power sources

A photovoltaic (PV) power source generates power by converting the Sun's solar energy into an electrical potential difference. This potential difference can then be used to power a variety of electrical appliances.

A PV module consists of many solar cells. Each solar cell is manufactured using a semiconductor material such as silicon. The cell is typically constructed from a 1 mm thick wafer of very pure silicon. Minute quantities of phosphorus and boron atoms (impurity atoms) are added to the top and bottom surfaces of the wafer, respectively. The impurity atoms bond into the silicon crystal in place of some silicon atoms. Phosphorus atoms have 'spare' electrons that are not required for bonding with silicon atoms, and the electrons are free to move around as negative charge carriers. The boron atoms have insufficient electrons for bonding. The points where electrons are absent are called 'holes', these are free to move around as positive charge carriers. The top surface of the silicon wafer, which has had some phosphorus atoms added to it, is referred to as n-type silicon as it has excess negative charge carriers. The bottom surface of the silicon, which has had some boron atoms added, is called p-type silicon as it has excess positive charge carriers. This process of making n- and p-type silicon is called doping.

The excess electrons and holes meet in the middle of the wafer to form a p–n junction. Here, the electrons from the n-type silicon combine with the holes from the p-type silicon. This region now has no free electrons and is thus an insulator.

On either side of this region, the atoms in the n-type silicon are depleted of electrons, while the atoms in the p-type silicon are depleted of holes. This makes the atoms negatively and positively charged, setting up a local 'reverse' electric field.

When a photon of light is incident on the wafer it is absorbed in the p–n junction, transferring its energy to the electrons. The electrons and holes now have enough energy to separate and are pulled towards the n- and p-type silicon, respectively, by the reverse electric field. The n-type

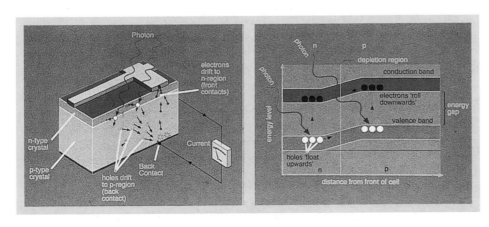

A silicon photovoltaic cell

silicon is now negatively charged, whereas the p-type silicon is positively charged. As more light enters, electrons and holes collect in the n- and p-type silicon. This generates a potential difference, which can power an external circuit.

Energy input

As you know, the Sun's energy consists of electromagnetic radiation, made up primarily of visible light and infrared radiation, but with ultraviolet radiation as well. A PV cell will generate electricity when visible and infrared radiation of wavelength between 350 and 1100 nm is incident upon its surface. Infrared radiation of wavelength greater than 1100 nm has no power generating effect.

Energy output

A PV module generates a d.c. potential difference. A particular module is designed to provide a particular voltage and this will depend on the number of cells connected together in the module. Like most power supplies, the potential difference generated decreases as the current

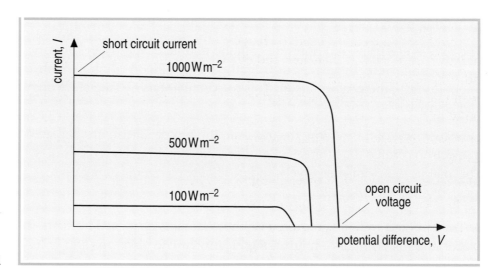

Figure 8.2
I–V characteristics of a silicon solar cell

drawn by the load connected to it increases. The way in which the potential difference and current change is displayed in the distinctive *I–V* characteristics shown in Figure 8.2.

As the power generated is equal to the product of *I* and *V*, most power is generated when the PV module is operating at the 'knee' of the curve. Optimum operation will be achieved when the resistance of the load is such that the panel operates at this point. A PV cell will typically have a power generating efficiency of 10–15%.

As the solar energy becomes more intense, the power generated by the PV module will increase. This is illustrated by an increase in the peak current on Figure 8.2.

Applications

PV systems can be designed to generate power from a few watts to several kilowatts. Thus, the generated power can be used for a variety of applications. However, their large-scale use is generally viable only when grid electricity is unavailable, as capital costs are relatively high. Furthermore, a great number of panels are required to generate large amounts of power.

The main advantage of PV power supplies lies in their ability to generate power in isolated locations while requiring little maintenance. They play an important role in many space applications, providing the power for artificial satellites. They also generate power for the operation of telecommunication repeater stations, offshore sea buoys, railway signal equipment, cathodic corrosion protection for pipelines and meteorological data collection apparatus.

Small-scale PV modules can be highly mobile and are easily installed. They have great potential in developing countries where small amounts of power will result in substantial benefits to people living in remote regions. In such areas, possible applications include lighting, water pumping and purification, and refrigeration.

Q2 A 12 V PV module is used to charge a 12 V lead–acid battery of charge capacity 50 A h. The area and efficiency of the module are 2.0 m^2 and 10%, respectively. The charging efficiency of the battery is 80%. The mean rate at which solar energy arrives during the 12 hours of daylight is 400 W m^{-2}.

(a) What is the mean electrical power generated by the module during daylight?

(b) What is the electrical power charging the battery?

(c) How long will it take to fully charge the battery?

(d) The charged battery is required to power a number of 8 W lamps connected in parallel for 7 hours a night. How many lamps can be connected? ◆

Q3 A PV cell generates power when radiation of wavelength 350–1100 nm is incident upon its surface. What is the minimum photon energy required to excite the cell? (Speed of light in a vacuum $= 3.0 \times 10^{-8}$ m s^{-1}, Planck's constant $h = 6.6 \times 10^{-34}$ J s.) ◆

Exploration 8.1 A flat solar panel

2 HOURS

Apparatus:

- dark garden hose attached to cold tap with outlet to tank
- means of measuring inlet and outlet temperature
- means of varying flow rate ◆ sheet of glass to cover hose
- polystyrene insulation for beneath hose ◆ measuring jug
- timer ◆ thermometers ◆ meter to measure insolation

Wear gardening gloves to handle the glass and take care not to stress any glass fittings.

Do this exploration on a sunny day with the Sun as high in the sky as possible.

Coil the hose and place it on the polystyrene on the ground or on an inclined board, then cover it with the glass sheet. (If a board is used to support the hose, try to ensure that the sunlight strikes it as near to perpendicular as possible.)

Measure the area of hose exposed to the Sun, the altitude angle of Sun, inlet temperature, outlet temperature and water flow rate and, using a suitable meter, insolation (the rate of solar energy supply per unit area) in $W\,m^{-2}$.

Set up a table and calculate the internal energy gain of water, the rate of solar energy supply and efficiency.

Vary the flow rate and repeat until you have sufficient readings to plot an efficiency versus temperature graph.

How does it compare with the graph you drew for Question 1?

Now remove the glass plate and repeat the process above. Compare your new graph with the first one you obtained. Remove the insulation and repeat again. Compare all three graphs.

Exploration 8.2 A concentrating collector: parabolic trough

2 HOURS

Apparatus:

- blockboard or plywood ◆ small saw ◆ heavy card
- cooking foil ◆ 12 mm copper pipe ◆ 30 mm glass tube
- aluminium (silver) paint ◆ paintbrush ◆ hose
- collection vessel ◆ thermometers ◆ measuring jug ◆ timer
- tacks ◆ rubber bungs ◆ cork borers ◆ drill and rasps

Using the formula $y^2 = 4ax$ generate parabola coordinates (using a spreadsheet if you wish). (Remember that square roots have positive and negative values.) The focus of this parabola is found at $(a, 0)$. Using the value $a = 20$ cm, mark up two of these parabolas on blockboard or plywood and cut them out.

Do not crimp the hose or reduce flow rate to zero: the water can boil and generate high pressures. Do not place any parts of your body, especially your eyes, within the reflection device, especially near the focus line. Do not stare at the Sun. Do not hold corks in the palm of your hand when using a cork boring tool.

Cut holes at coordinates (20 cm, 0), i.e. at the focus, in order
to fit the glass tube between the two blockboard parabolas. Cover the card with
aluminium foil, and tack this to the parabolas. The aperture should be about 1 m^2.
Oxidize the copper pipe over a Bunsen flame, insert it into the glass tube and fix it in
place using the bored bungs, then push the ends of the pipe into the holes in the
blockboard. Paint the front third of the outside of the glass tube silver. Figure 8.3 shows
the set up.

Point the assembly towards the Sun, inclining it so that the shadow of the tube lies
midway along the reflector and no shadow of the parabolas forms inside the assembly,
connect the ends of the copper tube to the hose so that you can run water through the
tube.

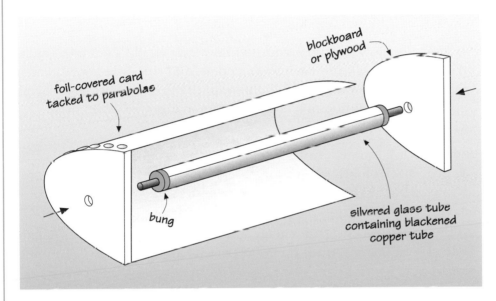

Figure 8.3
Set up for
Exploration 8.2

As the experiment progresses, you will have to adjust the angle of the assembly.

Conduct an experiment similar to Exploration 8.1 for the flat panel, but this time plot
efficiency against flow rate.

Do a calculation to decide if radiative heat loss accounts for the efficiency being less
than 100%.

 What are the advantages and disadvantages of the parabolic trough compared
with a flat collector?

The parabolic trough can be made to track the Sun and has increased efficiency
over that of a flat collector. However, it involves a higher level of technology and
expense and it will not be able to collect diffuse radiation.

Questions 4–7 refer to your parabolic collector. Our answers use typical values, but you will have to substitute your own values in our working to check your answer

Q4   How does the radiation loss rate for your exploration compare with the rate of solar energy supply (900 W m^{-2}) for the pipe at 90°C and at 300°C? (Assume your pipe to be a perfect black body with $\varepsilon = 1$, $\sigma = 5.7 \times 10^{-8}$ W m^{-2} K^{-4}; assume the pipe to be 1 m long and 12 mm in diameter) ◆

Q5   Estimate an appropriate mass flow rate for a 1.0 m^2 collector, given an inlet temperature of 10°C and an outlet temperature of 90°C. (Take the rate of solar energy supply to be 900 W m^{-2}, as before). ◆

Q6   How should the trough be aligned and 'driven' to capture the most Sun? ◆

Q7   At zero flow rate, approximately how long would a full tube (radius 6 mm) of water take to reach boiling point from 10°C; use your radiation rate for 90°C for now, even though it will vary from below this to slightly above? (*Note:* This question emphasizes the dangers of pipe blockages.) ◆

Q8   In 1923, inspired by the method used by Archimedes to ward off a Roman attack on his beloved Syracuse, an engineer managed to set fire to a rowing boat 50 m away with 70 plane mirrors, each with an area of 1.5 m^2.

(a) Work out the total solar energy striking the mirrors by multiplying the rate of solar energy arrival at mirrors per unit area (600 W m^{-2}) by mirror area.

(b) If all this is concentrated by the mirrors, each 65% efficient as reflectors, on to 1.5 m^2, what is the rate of supply of energy to the target?

(c) The target warms up until thermal radiation equilibrium is attained. What equilibrium temperature results if the boat is a perfect black body? (For a perfect black body $\varepsilon = 1$, $\sigma = 5.7 \times 10^{-8}$ W m^{-2} K^{-4}.) ◆

8.2 Wind power

As discussed in Section 7, the Sun is also responsible for the existence of wind – about 5.5% of the Sun's energy causes the differences in temperature and pressure in the atmosphere that drive the winds over Earth's surface. The power in the wind is proportional to the cube of the windspeed, so in Britain the useful power in the air passing through 1 m^2 can easily exceed 600 W.

Wind turbine aerodynamics

Wind turbines (other than those that are simply 'blown around' by the wind) exploit **lift**. This lift force is generated by the aerofoil blade section

Darrieus | H - type VAWT | V - type VAWT

Vertical axis wind turbines

of the turbine, which generates a pressure difference between its 'surfaces', which acts perpendicularly to the air flow. Wind turbines generally have two orientations: either their axis is horizontal and the wind approaches (in ideal conditions) in a direction parallel to this axis perpendicular to the plane in which the blades travel, or their axis and blade are vertical and the wind approaches perpendicular to both. For wind turbines lift is rarely just a vertical force. Lift increases with area of blade, density of air and the square of the air flow's velocity *relative to the blade*.

Why do you think penguins' wings are so small?

Because they fly underwater, not in the air! Water is much denser (about 1000 times more dense) than air, so for a given size and speed, lift is greater. This also means that hydrofoils are always much smaller than aerofoils for a given lift.

In fact lift, L, area of blade, A, density of air, ρ, and velocity, v, are related by the formula $L = \frac{1}{2}C_L\rho A v_{WB}^2$

A horizontal axis wind turbine

where the constant of proportionality C_L is the **coefficient of lift** and v_{WB} means velocity of wind relative to blade.

Figure 8.4(b) shows a blade moving up the page with velocity v_{BG} (velocity of blade relative to ground). Notice how the blade 'sees' the wind as coming from an angle. You have probably experienced this if you have cycled in a cross-wind. The faster you go, the more the wind seems to approach from ahead.

What is the direction of the lift force?

At right angles to v_{WB}.

All objects experience a **drag** force, D, when moving through air or another fluid. This points in the same direction as v_{WB} and is shown on Figure 8.4(a). Needless to say, engineers spend a lot of time ensuring lift is much larger than drag. For aerofoils, lift can be $100D$. Drag depends on the same quantities as lift so $D = \frac{1}{2}C_D \rho A v_{WB}^2$ where C_D is the

coefficient of drag. For the symmetrical aerofoil, C_D ranges from 0.006 to 0.024, for a car, $C_D \approx 0.3$–0.5. (Section 9.2, pages 136–45, of the SLIPP unit *Physics on the Move* has more information about aerodynamic drag.)

 What can you say about the vertical components of lift and drag?

They are opposed, but lift is much greater than drag, so the blade will accelerate.

Figure 8.4
Vertical axis wind turbine – perspective and plan views

 What can you say about the horizontal components?

They point to the right and both have a tendency to push the blade downwind.

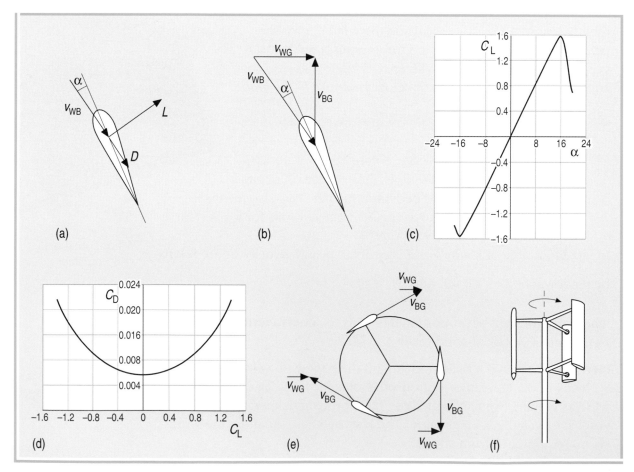

Measure angle α in Figure 8.4(b). For the symmetrical aerofoil, read off C_L and C_D using the graphs in Figure 8.4(c) and (d).

$\alpha \approx 10°$, $C_L \approx 1.0$ and $C_D \approx 0.012$.

If angle of attack, α, was greater than or equal to 16°, much loss of lift would occur but drag would remain, so the blade would slow down (this is called a stall). Modern wind turbines are designed to ensure lift remains a maximum, without stall, using **variable pitch blades**. Older windmills used sails that could shape themselves to the air flow.

 Refer to Figure 8.4(b). How does v_{BG} compare to v_{WG}?

---

v_{BG} is greater than or equal to v_{WG}. The blade goes faster than the wind.

A sail windmill

The maximum ratio $\dfrac{v_{BG}}{v_{WG}}$ is called the **tip speed ratio** and can approach values as high as 12. For this reason, a fairly narrow blade can 'process' more wind than you might think. (As an analogy, consider how a fast-moving narrow paint brush can lay as much paint as a slow-moving wide brush in a given time.)

Q9 A turbine with tip speed ratio 7 intercepts a 15 m s^{-1} wind. What speed will the tips attain? ◆

Q10 A plan view of a *vertical* axis turbine blade is shown in Figure 8.4(e), with symmetrical blades. Copy the figure and show (roughly to scale), v_{WB}, α, L and D and resultant force F on the blade in each position. The whole machine is shown in Figure 8.4(f). We have shown v_{WG} and v_{BG} in three positions for you. First add α and v_{WB} to your copy and check your answer. Then, remembering that L is perpendicular to v_{WB}, include this. D is in line with v_{WB}. Show this too, remembering that L and D are proportional to v^2 and L is very much greater than D. Finally, show the resultant force, F, which is given by

$F = L + D$

Notice that the tip speed ratio varies, stalling may occur if v_{BG} is too low, both sides of the blade approach the wind and all the Fs provide clockwise moments. ◆

In 1929, an engineer called Betz determined that the maximum efficiency of a turbine was achieved when the wind velocity was reduced from v to $\dfrac{v}{3}$ by the turbine. He assumed that the velocity at the turbine itself was the mean of these values, i.e.

velocity at turbine = average of input and output velocities

Q11 (a) What is the air velocity at the turbine?

(b) Imagine a cylinder of air length l and cross-section A. What is the mass of air (density, ρ) in this cylinder?

(c) If this cylinder represents the air passing a point in one second, how are l and v related?

(d) What is the kinetic energy in this cylinder of air? (That is, the kinetic energy intercepted by the turbine per second, or the power in the wind.)

(e) What is the mass of air passing the turbine per second? (Remember that the windspeed is $\frac{2}{3}v$ at the turbine.)

(f) What is its momentum change per second of air passing through turbine? (Remember that this air slows from v down to $\frac{1}{3}v$.) (*Note:* Newton's second law states that force equals rate of change of momentum, so your answer also gives the force on the turbine.)

(g) Under steady conditions, power, $P =$ force $\times$ velocity. What power is developed at the turbine?

(h) How does this compare with the power arriving at the turbine? In other words, what is the maximum efficiency of the turbine?

(i) Blades of vertical axis machines intercept the airstream twice. How will this affect efficiency? (No calculations are needed.) ◆

Heavy blades being lifted into position on a wind turbine at Grandpa's Knob, USA

As mentioned in the answer to Question 11, the windmill or turbine cannot extract all the energy in the wind. The optimum theoretical efficiency is about 60% under the conditions outlined above, but in practice values rarely exceed 30%. This limitation on efficiency is not the only problem – winds do not arrive at turbines in a steady flow in one direction, they change direction and much of their energy is contained in damaging gusts, so wind turbines must be engineered to accommodate these. (An early prototype turbine at Grandpa's Knob in the USA shed a one tonne blade during a gale. It was hurled 230 m before lodging itself in the ground.)

A one tonne blade blown from the wind turbine at Grandpa's Knob during a gale

Another problem is the amount of space that they require. A 1300 MW wind park requires up to 40 km² of land containing several generators. Despite this, such wind farms exist in California, the UK and Denmark, although their siting causes much criticism from some local residents, who complain that they are an eyesore and noisy.

Q12 Confirm that in $P = \dfrac{1}{2}\rho A v^3$ the units of the right hand side are watts. ◆

 If the windspeed doubles, by how much does the power developed by the turbine increase?

By eight times.

Q13 Taking $A = 1\text{m}^2$ and $\rho = 1.3 \text{ kg m}^{-3}$, what is the mean power in the wind (per unit area) for the 'regime' in Table 8.1? Use median values for each speed range. ◆

Table 8.1 Frequency of wind direction (%) and speed at Farnborough, latitude 50° 17'N, longitude 00°45'W

Mean windspeed/ m s^{-1}	\multicolumn{12}{c}{% of time speed occurs at each clockwise bearing, in degrees from north}	% of time speed occurs
	350–10	20–40	50–70	80–100	110–130	140–160	170–190	200–220	230–250	260–280	290–310	320–340	
0													3.2
0–1.4	0.9	0.7	0.6	1.1	1.0	1.2	1.2	1.4	2.0	1.9	2.0	1.2	15.2
1.4–3.2	1.7	1.9	1.6	1.7	1.3	1.8	1.8	2.0	3.8	2.8	2.4	1.5	24.3
3.2–5.4	1.6	2.8	2.3	1.8	1.1	1.8	2.0	3.5	5.2	3.7	2.2	2.0	30.0
5.4–8.0	0.6	1.3	1.1	0.7	0.4	0.8	1.6	3.7	3.0	2.2	1.3	1.3	18.0
8.0–10.6			0.1	0.1		0.1	0.4	0.8	0.2	0.3	0.2	0.1	2.3

 A generator attached to a wind turbine with 5.0 m blades is 80% efficient. What mean electrical power would be developed in Farnborough if the turbine is 40% efficient?

Total efficiency = $0.8 \times 0.4 = 0.32$ or 32%
From Question 13

input power $= 64.67 \text{ W m}^{-2} \times \pi(5.0\text{m})^2$

$= 5079 \text{ W}$

output power $= 0.32 \times 5079 \text{ W}$

$= 1.6 \times 10^3 \text{ W}$ (to two significant figures)

Exploration 8.3   Building a Savonius-rotor wind-powered car and investigating its effectiveness

2 HOURS

When cut, tinplate cans are very sharp. When handling the car, wear protective gloves.

Apparatus:

◆ large coffee tin ◆ Meccano ◆ soldering iron and solder ◆ stopwatch ◆ file

Build a chassis out of Meccano with a vertical shaft driving one set of wheels, as shown in Figure 8.5. Cut the coffee tin and lid in half, blunt the edges with a file and solder the lids into the half tins. Using Meccano, mount the tin halves on the vertical shaft.

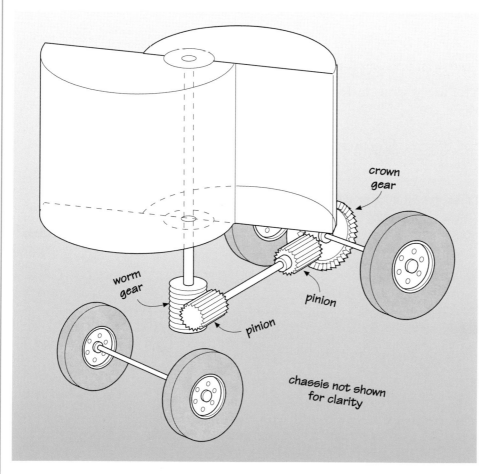

crown gear

worm gear

pinion

pinion

chassis not shown for clarity

Figure 8.5
Savonius's wind car

Part (i)

Place the car on smooth ground in the wind. With a stopwatch, time your car (a) into the wind, (b) downwind, (c) with a cross-wind. Calculate the speed of your car in each case.

Part (ii)

Vary the gear ratios and try again.

Part (iii)

Vary the overlap of the cans and try again.

TECHNICAL NOTE

When Captain Savonius invented this type of turbine he simply connected two different configurations to the same shaft in opposition and saw which way the shaft turned.

By doing this he was comparing starting torque (the initial turning effect of the wind when the turbine is stationary). Savonius rotors are self-starting, but they are not especially efficient. However, they are simple in design, they are omnidirectional and power can be extracted at ground level from the vertical axis. You may have seen them used as ventilators on van roofs.

Q14 Look back at the data in Table 8.1.

(a) By searching for maximum percentages, find where, approximately, prevailing winds come from.

(b) What does the bottom row of data suggest about the design of a wind turbine? ◆

Look at the data on the maps in Figure 8.6(a) and (b) and answer the following questions.

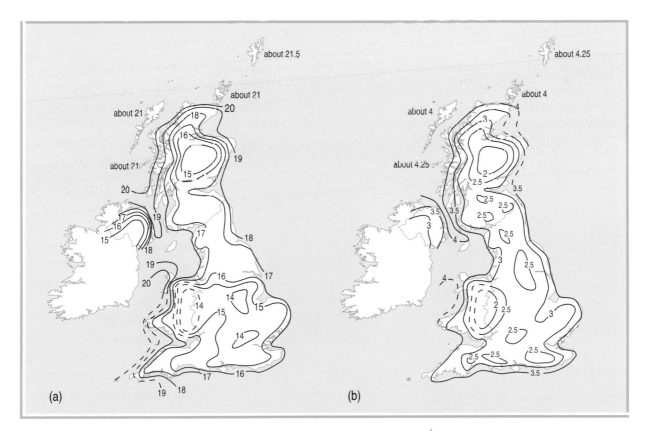

(a)   (b)

Figure 8.6 Maps of the UK showing hourly mean windspeeds in m s^{-1} for the years 1965–74: (a) speed exceeded for 0.1% of the time; (b) speed exceeded for 75% of the time

How much greater are the *forces* on a turbine blade in a wind of 6 m s^{-1} wind as compared with those on a blade in a wind of 3 m s^{-1}?

Force $\propto v^2$, so the force is four times as great.

 What implications for wind turbine design do the maps reveal?

While wind speeds are generally modest, for 1/1000th of the time very severe winds are encountered. Turbines must be able to be braked to a halt and they must be structurally sound, so as to avoid damage.

 Where are the best sites for wind power in the UK?

The coasts of northern Scotland and offshore Wales seem to be the best sites if turbines are engineered properly.

Q15 Using Figure 8.6(b), estimate what power per metre^2 can be intercepted in the Pennines for most of the year. ◆

8.3 Wave energy

Solar energy indirectly creates wave energy. Solar energy generates winds, which in turn sweep over the surface of the sea generating waves. The quantity of energy imparted by the wind to the sea depends on how strong the wind is, the time for which the wind blows and the fetch – the distance over which the wind and water interact.

The British Isles is fortunate in having coastlines that have energetic waves. This is particularly true of the Atlantic-facing coasts, where every metre of **wavefront** generates tens of thousands of kilowatts. Wave energy therefore has a major contribution to make to our energy needs. Figure 8.7 shows the average wave energy contours around the British Isles.

Figure 8.7
Average wave energy contours. The data show the annual energy in MW h, and the bracketed figures are the power intensities in kW m^{-1} – the rate of energy supply per unit length of wave

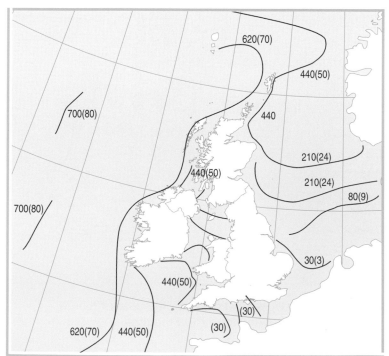

Wave energy converters

Attempts have been made to harness wave energy for at least 200 years, but it was the onset of the 1973 oil crisis that galvanized research in this area.

Shallow water waves are **transverse waves**. The direction of the oscillating water particles is at 90° to the direction of the wave energy. Water waves have both kinetic energy, by virtue of their motion, and gravitational potential energy, by virtue of the height of the wave.

In deep water sea waves the nature of the particle motion is more complicated than in a simple transverse wave. A deep water wave is defined as one in which the depth is greater than half the wave's wavelength. The profile of such a wave is shown in Figure 8.8. In the upper zone the particles follow a circular orbit, further down the orbit becomes more elliptical, and deeper still the particle motion is linear. In other words, at depth the wave motion is essentially that of a **longitudinal wave**. The aim of a wave energy converter is to capture the energy in the top layer.

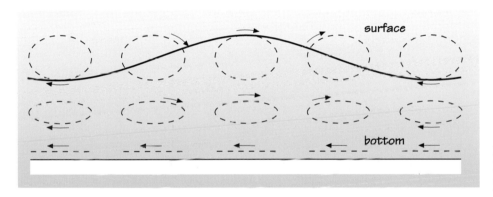

Figure 8.8
Deep water wave profile

In shallow coastal waves, where the depth of the wave is less than half the wavelength, the power of the waves reduces rapidly because the lower orbits are affected by friction with the sea-bed.

The position and type of energy converter will have to match the behaviour of the water.

Q16   It is suggested that the velocity of water waves, v, depends on the acceleration due to gravity, g, and the wavelength, λ. Which of the following formulae are definitely wrong? (a) $v = \dfrac{k\lambda}{g}$; (b) $v = kg\lambda$;

(c) $v = k\sqrt{\lambda g}$ (k is a constant and it has no units). ◆

Many different types of converting devices have been designed; we will take a look at two of them – 'Salter's duck' and the oscillating air column.

Salter's duck

Professor Salter of Edinburgh University investigated the possibilities of harnessing the energy of water waves using a mechanical hydraulic device. It is called a 'duck' because of its nodding oscillatory behaviour. It moves with the motion of the waves and is designed to 'capture' the wave's energy as it passes. The ducks consist of a line of cone-shaped vanes fixed to a central shaft, and the oscillatory motion of the device drives a rotatory pump, which powers a generator. Salter's duck can extract energy from the sea at a rate of 50 MW per kilometre length of energy capturing device.

Salter's duck

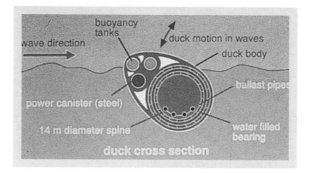

The Department of Energy abandoned this line of research in 1982, because of the allegedly high development costs.

The oscillating air column

For several years Trevor Whitaker's team, based at Queen's University, Belfast, has been researching the potential of harnessing wave energy using a structure called an oscillating air column, as illustrated in Figure 8.9. The water inside the column rises as the crest of the wave rises (Figure 8.9a). The air above this water is compressed and is forced past the turbine from left to right. The water inside the column then falls as the crest of the wave falls and air is pushed into the column by the excess pressure outside (Figure 8.9b). Again the air flows unidirectionally from left to right. Note how the valve system functions.

Whitaker's team have constructed such a device on the Hebridean island of Islay that can generate up to 75 kW.

Figure 8.9
Oscillating air column

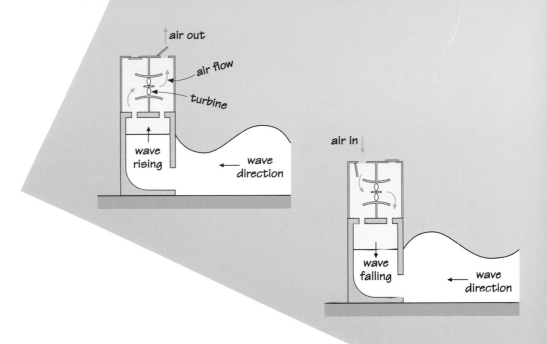

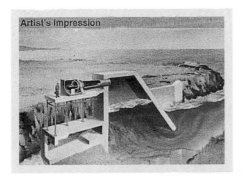

Oscillating air column on Islay

The first commercial wave energy converter, code-named 'Osprey', was an oscillating air column. It was sited off the coast of Scotland at Dounreay and put in place in 1995. Unfortunately, it was damaged in transit and sank in heavy seas – a testimony to the vagaries of wave-regime and the cruelty of the sea!

From an engineering viewpoint, designing the means to harness wave energy is not easy. If you stand by the sea and observe the structure of the waves you will appreciate the variability of wave height, power, wavelength and wave-speed.

One benefit of extracting wave energy is that 'behind' the extracting device, the **amplitude** and energy of the waves is less. This is a very beneficial effect as far as coastal shipping and sea defences are concerned.

8.4 Tidal power

Tides are caused mainly by the Moon's gravitational pull and partly by the Sun's, and they can be affected by the action of wind on the water. Tidal flows experience friction with the sea-bed and are causing Earth's spin rate to decrease, by one second per day approximately every 20 000 years. In its strictest sense, then, tidal power is a depleting source!

Methods of harnessing tidal power have been around for hundreds of years: tidemills were mentioned in the Domesday Book in 1086 and there were still about a dozen medieval-style tidemills running in the UK in 1939.

More recently, the French have built a tidal barrage in the Rance estuary, near St Malo. The tidal flow drives bi-directional turbines while ebbing and flowing, developing an average of 65 MW. However, problems exist with this technique – tides with a 25 h cycle do not synchronize with the 24 h cycle of our lifestyles and the times of maximum energy demands. Also, the ecological consequences of such large-scale devices could be immense; for example, they may damage the shoreline habitats for birds. Interest is still active in the UK though, and the proposed Severn and Mersey barrages are rated at 8600 and 660 MW, respectively, or 7–8% of current electricity demand.

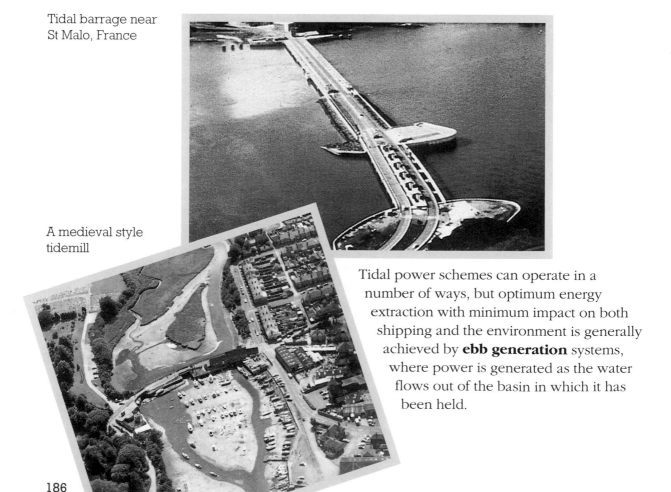

Tidal barrage near St Malo, France

A medieval style tidemill

Tidal power schemes can operate in a number of ways, but optimum energy extraction with minimum impact on both shipping and the environment is generally achieved by **ebb generation** systems, where power is generated as the water flows out of the basin in which it has been held.

Q17 (a) Using Figure 8.10, work out the available potential energy in the trapped water behind the proposed Cardiff Weston Line Barrage in the Severn estuary at high tide, if the water outside has fallen to low tide. (Mean tidal range is 7.0 m. Approximate the size of the estuary to a 15×50 km triangle. Use $g = 9.8$ m s^{-1} and density of seawater, $\rho = 1.0 \times 10$ kg m^{-3})

(b) Why cannot all this energy be converted into electrical energy?

(c) Suppose this energy can be converted in the subsequent 5 hours at 90% efficiency. What power is developed? ◆

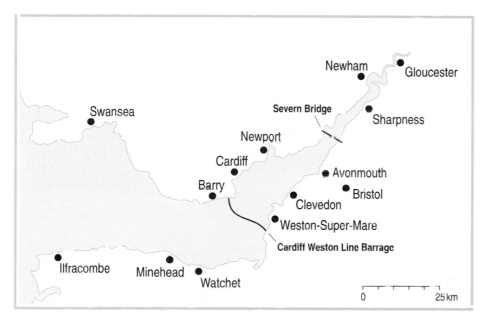

Figure 8.10 Proposed siting of the Cardiff Weston Line Barrage

8.5 Hydroelectric power

A problem with all 'income sources' of energy is their variability – in the UK the Sun shines mostly in the summer and during the day. The wind blows mostly in the winter and tides do not have a 24 h period. Nevertheless, researchers believe that around 20–30% of our electricity supply could be supplied by these variable sources, without the need for storage capacity, because of the absorbing power of the national grid. When, for example, one windmill is becalmed, it is likely that others elsewhere will be working. However, if energy storage *is* needed, one resource with inbuilt storage capacity is **hydroelectric power**. The physical principles associated with the extraction of power from water are the same as for wind. However, in large hydroelectric power schemes with dams, the resulting reservoir of water acts as a large storage device.

The energy stored in a dam is effectively solar power – the Sun's rays evaporate water, which condenses and falls as rain after which it can be collected behind a dam. As this water is released, gravitational potential energy does work driving a turbine, which itself drives a generator (alternator). Figure 8.11 shows a typical hydroelectric scheme.

Again, hydroelectric power (HEP) is not free – building a dam is an enormous engineering project that can cost hundreds of millions of

Figure 8.11
A hydroelectric scheme

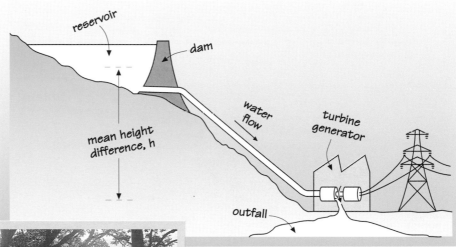

pounds. But rain is free and maintenance costs are very low. Financially, the controversial HEP schemes of the 1960s now supply our cheapest electricity. Officially, most of the economic sites for HEP have already been exploited. However, thousands of sites exist for small-scale, possibly private, exploitation, though the idea that big is best is still prevalent. The Energy Act of 1983 now requires electricity companies to buy back the surpluses of small-scale generators, which should provide an incentive to develop more marginal sites.

A hydroelectric power station on the River Tay at Pitlochry, Scotland

Q18 A lake of area 7.0 km^2, with mean depth 96 m is connected by a 2.0 m diameter pipe to a turbine 750 m vertically below the bottom of the dam, as illustrated in Figure 8.11. Estimate: (a) the energy stored in the dam; (b) the mean power supplied to the turbine if the flow rate is 46 m^3 s^{-1}; (c) how long the lake can provide energy; (d) the mean linear fluid flow speed. (Use $g = 9.8$ m s^{-1} and density of water, $\rho = 1.0 \times 10$ kg m^{-3}) ◆

The storage ability of hydroelectric generators can be further enhanced by pump storage schemes. In such schemes, when electricity demand is

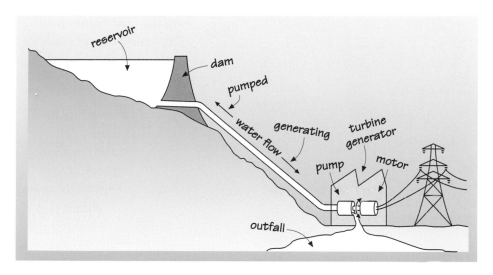

Figure 8.12
A pump storage scheme

A pump storage scheme at Cruachan, Scotland

low, the turbines are used as pumps, powered by electric motors, to move water from a lower reservoir to an upper one (see Figure 8.12). Then, at times of peak demand, this stored energy can be delivered. These schemes exploit the fact that it is much quicker to switch hydroelectric plant on and off (perhaps as short a time as 8 s is required) than thermal or nuclear generators.

8.6 Solar ponds

Inspired by natural saline ponds like the Dead Sea, **solar ponds** have been developed to capture and store solar energy. The mechanism they use is quite simple – as the water absorbs thermal energy, a higher concentration of salt dissolves into it, the water becomes more dense and then sinks, taking the stored thermal energy with it. This is the opposite of a freshwater lake, in which the warm water rises, to lose heat at the

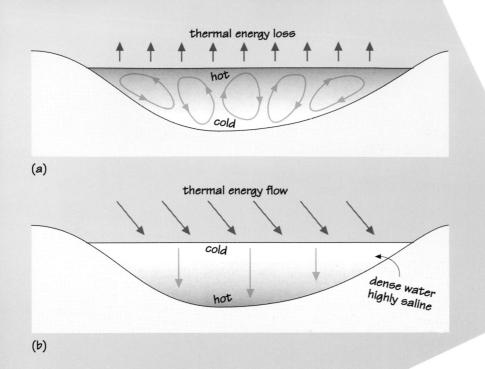

(a)

(b)

surface (see Figure 8.13). Water in solar ponds can attain very high temperatures, sometimes approaching 100°C, and they can maintain their temperature throughout the winter. Energy may be extracted by using a heat-pump and/or a heat exchanger.

Figure 8.13
(a) A freshwater lake compared with (b) a solar pond

8.7 Geothermal energy

Much of the interior of the Earth is hot and contains materials undergoing **radioactive decay**. Tectonic plates sliding against each other cause heating by friction. Solidification of the interior of the Earth liberates **latent heat**. Consequently, there is a steady flow of geothermal energy entering the biosphere through the Earth's crust.

These effects can be observed in the natural hot water geysers of Iceland, for example. The idea of tapping this resource by pumping fluid through the warm rocks previously cracked with explosions is an attractive one, but the rate at which we would need to extract energy for this to be economic would far exceed the natural rate of supply from below (in UK this is about 60 mW m^{-2}). So geothermal energy must generally be considered yet another capital energy resource (though within its lifetime it is a firm and predictable source of continuous power). It has been used for district heating in France, Iceland, and Hungary, and an Italian electric power station using geothermal energy sources was built in 1904. Unfortunately, in the UK the **temperature gradient** is rather low – 30°C km^{-1}, so bore holes need to be deep for a high enough temperature to be reached.

Geothermally generated electrical capacity is predicted to supply about 75 GW worldwide by the year 2000.

8.8 Summary

The major argument against the use of renewable resources of energy is their **dispersion**, and variability. It is estimated that replacing one 1000 MW power station would require 20 km of tidal barrage or wave generators and 40 km^2 of solar voltaic collectors (i.e. 4 miles × 4 miles). This, however, assumes centralized generation, and because tidal barrage, wave generators or solar collectors are unfirm supplies, the grid remains essential. Certainly the benefits of cogeneration seem more attainable than a wholesale alternative strategy.

Q19 Suppose every one of our 40 000 pylons in the UK were a wind turbine, what mass generating capacity would we have (for no extra land use) for a windspeed of $v = 5$ m s^{-1} for 25% of the time. Assume they are 50 m radius and 40% efficient. ◆

Q20 For a housing stock of 24 million houses, work out the thermal energy that roof mounted solar collectors could generate, given a mean annual insolation of 1000 kW h m^{-2} yr^{-1}. (Suppose a useful roof area is 4 m × 4 m, on average, and the collectors are 75% efficient.) ◆

Geysers

Achievements

After working through this section you should be able to:

- describe various methods to make direct use of solar radiation, including the structure of solar cells (electrical) and solar panels (thermal)
- appreciate the importance of effective cheap storage of energy
- estimate the power available from a wind generator
- describe different ways of harnessing the wind, and discuss the disadvantages and problems of an intermittent source
- appreciate the difficulty of harnessing wave energy and be able to describe one device that achieves it
- estimate the power available from a water wave of given dimensions
- calculate the potential energy stored in a lake
- note one solution to the problem of daily and seasonal variations in demand for electrical power
- describe a typical hydroelectric and pumped storage project, including the advantages and disadvantages of dams and lakes
- estimate the mean power output of a tidal barrage
- distinguish between tidal flows and rivers as energy sources
- describe geothermal energy
- distinguish between firm and unfirm, predictable and unpredictable sources.

Glossary

Amplitude The maximum magnitude of a wavelike quantity.

Capital sources Energy resources that when depleted are not replaced, or are replaced at a very low rate (such as fossil fuels).

Coefficient of drag Symbol: C_D. The dimensionless constant linking drag force, D, to area, A, fluid density, ρ, and relative velocity, v, in the following equation:

$$D = \frac{1}{2}C_D \rho A v^2.$$

Coefficient of lift Symbol: C_L. The dimensionless constant relating lift force, L, to air density, ρ, air speed, v, and wing area, A, in the following equation:

$$L = \frac{1}{2}C_L \rho A v^2.$$

Concentrating collector A Sun-tracking solar collector using solar energy to vaporize a working fluid (e.g. water under reduced pressure), which will then power turbines to drive generators. This has the efficiency of a typical thermal power station but, because of its level of technical complication and cost, is likely to be used only for large centralized schemes.

Dispersion In the context of energy sources, dispersion is an indication of concentration . Highly dispersed sources like solar power are not concentrated. A fuel is a concentrated source. Unit for wind and solar power: $W\ m^{-2}$; unit for waves: $W\ m^{-1}$ (power per unit length of wavefront).

Drag Unit: newton (N); symbol: D. The force between a body and a fluid in relative motion that acts so as to oppose the motion.

Ebb generation Generation of electricity from tidal variations in water level that uses power generated by water flowing out of a basin in which it has been held. This type of tidal generation combines optimum energy extraction with the minimum impact on shipping and the environment.

Hydroelectric power Electrical power generated from passing water falling under gravity through a water turbine.

Income sources   Energy resources that are constantly replenished (such as solar energy and hydroelectric power).

Latent heat   Unit: joule (J). Literally means 'hidden heat' – the energy absorbed or emitted during a change of state (phase), such as melting/fusion or vaporization/condensation. Associated with the breaking/making of bonds and/or expansion/contraction of a vapour. The word 'hidden', is really a misnomer because the effects of latent heat may be perfectly apparent.

Lift   Unit: newton (N); symbol: L. The force generated by the section of an aerofoil blade in motion relative to the surrounding fluid that acts at right angles to the fluid flow. It is the result of the pressure difference in the fluid between the two surfaces of the blade.

Longitudinal wave   A wave having the direction of its oscillations in the direction of its propagation.

Radioactive decay   The spontaneous transformation of atoms of one radioactive (parent) nuclide into another (daughter) nuclide. The process results in an exponential decay that decreases the number of parent atoms.

Solar pond   A volume of saline water that can be used to capture and store thermal energy. When its temperature rises, more salt dissolves into solution, the warm liquid becomes denser and therefore sinks. A high temperature may be maintained and the thermal energy may be extracted by a heat pump and/or a heat exchanger.

Temperature gradient   Units: degrees Celsius per metre ($°C\,m^{-1}$) or kelvin per metre ($K\,m^{-1}$). A region in which temperature changes with displacement.

Tip speed ratio   The ratio of blade tip speed to windspeed (both relative to the ground).

Transverse wave   A wave having the direction of its oscillation at right angles to the direction of its propagation.

Unfirm   Unpredictable during a specific short time interval.

Variable pitch blades   Blades designed so that their angle relative to the wind can be adjusted.

Wavefront   A hypothetical surface over which the oscillations emitted by a source are in phase.

Answers to Ready to Study test

R1

(a) The resultant force acting on the cycle is the active force from the cyclist minus frictional forces acting on the cycle.

From Newton's second law of motion

resultant force on cycle = mass × acceleration

$$acceleration = \frac{velocity\ change}{time\ taken}$$
$$= \frac{9.0\,ms^{-1} - 3.0\,ms^{-1}}{12\,s}$$
$$= 0.5\,ms^{-2}$$

so

$$resultant\ force = 75\,kg \times 0.5\,ms^{-2}$$
$$= 37.5\,N$$
$$= 38\,N$$
(to two significant figures)

(b) The tractive force supplied at the rear wheel is given by

tractive force $= 37.5\,\text{N} + 15.0\,\text{N}$

$\qquad = 52.5\,\text{N}$

$\qquad = 53\,\text{N}\,(\text{to two significant figures})$

(c) Using the constant acceleration equation

$$2as = v^2 - u^2$$

where $a = 0.5\text{ m s}^{-2}$, $v = 9.0\text{ m s}^{-1}$, $u = 3.0\text{ m s}^{-1}$, gives the distance travelled during the acceleration as

$$s = \frac{\left(9.0\,\text{ms}^{-1}\right)^2 - \left(3.0\,\text{ms}^{-1}\right)^2}{2\times 0.5\,\text{ms}^{-2}}$$

$$= \frac{81\,\text{m}^2\,\text{s}^{-2} - 9\,\text{m}^2\,\text{s}^{-2}}{2\times 0.5\,\text{ms}^{-2}}$$

$$= 72\,\text{m}$$

(d)

Work done by cyclist

$\qquad = \text{tractive force} \times \text{displacement}$

$\qquad = 52.5\,\text{N} \times 72.0\,\text{m}$

$\qquad = 3780\,\text{J}$

$\qquad = 3.8 \times 10^3\,\text{J}$

$\qquad$ (to two significant figures)

(e)

Mean power output of cyclist $= \dfrac{\text{work done}}{\text{time taken}}$

$\qquad = \dfrac{3780\,\text{J}}{12\,\text{s}}$

$\qquad = 315\,\text{W}$

$\qquad = 3.2 \times 10^2\,\text{W}$

$\qquad$ (to two significant figures)

R2

Volume of 2.0 litres $= 2 \times 1000 \times 10^{-6}\,\text{m}^3$

$\qquad = 2.0 \times 10^{-3}\,\text{m}^3$

Mass of water $= \text{density} \times \text{volume}$

$\qquad = 1000\,\text{kg m}^{-3} \times 2 \times 10^{-3}\,\text{m}^3$

$\qquad = 2.0\,\text{kg}$

Velocity of water jet

$\qquad = \dfrac{\text{volume of water per second}}{\text{cross-sectional area of nozzle}}$

$\qquad = \dfrac{2.0 \times 10^{-3}\,\text{m}^3\,\text{s}^{-1}}{2.0 \times 10^{-4}\,\text{m}^2}$

$\qquad = 10\,\text{ms}^{-1}$

From Newton's second law of motion:

force exerted by water

$\qquad = \text{rate of change of momentum}$

$\qquad = \text{mass flow per second} \times \text{original velocity}$

$\qquad = 2.0\,\text{kg s}^{-1} \times 10\,\text{ms}^{-1}$

$\qquad = 20\,\text{N}$

So the force experienced by the cyclist is 20 N.

R3

(a) The power delivered by the battery in 5.0 h is given by

$$P = IV$$

$\qquad = 0.40\,\text{A} \times 4.5\,\text{V}$

$\qquad = 1.8\,\text{W}$

Total energy delivery by the battery is

$$\text{energy} = \text{power} \times \text{time}$$

$$= 1.8\,\text{W} \times (5.0 \times 60 \times 60)\,\text{s}$$

$$= 3.24 \times 10^4\,\text{J}$$

$$= \frac{3.24 \times 10^4}{3.6 \times 10^6}\,\text{kW h}$$

$$= 9.0 \times 10^{-3}\,\text{kW h}$$

The cost of 9.0×10^{-3} kW h is £2.70, so

$$\text{cost of 1kW h} = \frac{£2.70}{9.0 \times 10^{-3}}$$

$$= £300$$

(b)

Charge flow $= It$

$$= 0.40\,\text{A} \times (5.0 \times 60 \times 60)\,\text{s}$$

$$= 7.2 \times 10^3\,\text{C}$$

R4

$E = hf$

and

$\lambda f = c$

so

$$E = \frac{hc}{\lambda}$$

The speed of light, c, is 3.0×10^8 m s^{-1} and Planck's constant, h, is 6.6×10^{-34} J s, so for $\lambda = 483$ nm

$$E_1 = \frac{6.6 \times 10^{-34}\,\text{J s} \times 3.0 \times 10^8\,\text{ms}^{-1}}{483 \times 10^{-9}\,\text{m}}$$

$$= 4.1 \times 10^{-19}\,\text{J (to two significant figures)}$$

and for $\lambda = 10\,\mu\text{m}$

$$E_2 = \frac{6.6 \times 10^{-34}\,\text{J s} \times 3.0 \times 10^8\,\text{ms}^{-1}}{10 \times 10^{-6}\,\text{m}}$$

$$= 2.0 \times 10^{-20}\,\text{J (to two significant figures)}$$

Answers to questions in the text

Q1

(a) Using

$$\varepsilon = 1 - \frac{5.0\left(\dfrac{\theta_{\text{out}} + \theta_{\text{in}}}{2} - \theta_{\text{sur}}\right)°\text{C}^{-1}}{600}$$

$$= 1 - \frac{5.0°\text{C}^{-1}\left(\dfrac{\theta_{\text{out}} + 10°\text{C}}{2} - 15°\text{C}\right)}{600}$$

$$= 1 - \left(\frac{2.5}{600}°\text{C}^{-1}\theta_{\text{out}} - \frac{50}{60}\right)$$

$$= -\frac{2.5}{600}°\text{C}^{-1}\theta_{\text{out}} + 1 + \frac{50}{60}$$

$$= -4.17 \times 10^{-3}°\text{C}^{-1}\theta_{\text{out}} + 1.0833$$

This is of the form

$y = mx + c$

and will result in a straight-line graph of gradient $-4.17 \times 10^{-3}°\text{C}^{-1}$ and intercept on y-axis at 1.0833, as shown in Figure 8.14.

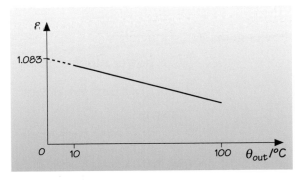

Figure 8.14 Answer to Question 1(a)

The graph has a negative gradient, so efficiency falls as a higher output temperature is demanded. This is because heat losses increase.

(b) When $\theta_{out} = 40°C$, $\varepsilon = 0.92$,

when $\theta_{out} = 70°C$, $\varepsilon = 0.79$,

when $\theta_{out} = 100°C$, $\varepsilon = 0.67$.

These can be found by calculation or from your graph.

(c) Returning to Equation (8.2) for ε:

$$\varepsilon = \frac{m'c(\theta_{out} - \theta_{in})}{600\,W\,m^{-2}A}$$

$\varepsilon = 0.79$ from part (b), $\theta_{out} = 70°C$, $\theta_{in} = 10°C$, $A = 1\,m^2$.

Rearranging gives

$$m' = \frac{600\,J\,s^{-1}\,m^{-2}\,A\varepsilon}{c(\theta_{out} - \theta_{in})}$$

$$= \frac{600\,J\,s^{-1} \times 0.79}{4200\,J\,kg^{-1}\,K^{-1}(70-10)\,K}$$

$$= 1.9 \times 10^{-3}\,kg\,s^{-1}$$

(to two significant figures)

Q2

(a)

Power generated = efficiency

$$\times \text{power supply rate}$$

$$= 0.10 \times 2.0\,m^2 \times 400\,W\,m^{-2}$$

$$= 80\,W$$

(b)

Power charging the battery $= 0.80 \times 80\,W$

$$= 64\,W$$

(c) The energy required to fully charge the battery is

$$VIt = VQ$$

where $V = 12$ V

$It = 50$ A

$$= 50\,A \times 3600\,s$$

$$= 180\,000\,coulombs$$

Energy $= 12\,V \times 180\,000\,C$

$$= 2.16\,MJ$$

$$= 2.2\,MJ \text{ (to two significant figures)}$$

so

$$\text{time taken} = \frac{2.16 \times 10^6\,J}{64\,W}$$

$$= 33\,750\,s$$

$$= 9.4\,h \text{ (to two significant figures)}$$

(d)

Energy converted by n lamps

$$= n \times 8\,W \times 7 \times 3600\,s$$

$$= 201\,600n\,J$$

Since

$$201\,600n\,J = 2.16\,MJ$$

It follows that

$$n = \frac{2\,160\,000\,J}{201\,600\,J}$$

$$= 10.7$$

So ten lamps may be powered.

Q3

The longest wavelength is associated with the lowest photon energy. Using

$$E = hf$$

and

$$\lambda f = c$$

it follows that

$$E = \frac{hc}{\lambda}$$

Therefore

$$E = \frac{6.6 \times 10^{-34} \, \text{J s} \times 3.0 \times 10^8 \, \text{m s}^{-1}}{1100 \times 10^{-9} \, \text{m}}$$

$$= 1.8 \times 10^{-19} \, \text{J}$$

Q4

Stefan's law may be used, so radiation loss is given by

$$\rho = \varepsilon \sigma A T^4$$

If we assume that the pipe is a black body, then

$$\varepsilon = 1$$

$$\sigma = 5.7 \times 10^{-8} \, \text{W m}^{-2} \, \text{K}^{-4}$$

and

$$A = 2\pi r l$$

$$= 2\pi \times 6 \times 10^{-3} \, \text{m} \times 1 \, \text{m}$$

$$= 2\pi \times 6 \times 10^{-3} \, \text{m}^2$$

So

$$P = 5.7 \times 10^{-8} \, \text{W m}^{-2} \, \text{K}^{-4}$$

$$\times 2\pi \times 6 \times 10^{-3} \, \text{m}^2 \times T^4$$

$$= 2.15 \times 10^{-9} \, \text{W K}^{-4} \times T^4$$

at 90°C

$$P = 2.15 \times 10^{-9} \, \text{W K}^{-4} \times (90 + 273)^4 \, \text{K}^4$$

$$= 37 \, \text{W (to two significant figures)}$$

at 300°C

$$P = 2.15 \times 10^{-9} \, \text{W K}^{-4} \times (300 + 273)^4 \, \text{K}^4$$

$$= 232 \, \text{W}$$

$$= 2.3 \times 10^2 \, \text{W (to two significant figures)}$$

These are both small compared with the rate of solar energy supply, which is 900 W in this case. In fact, your pipe has been enclosed in a glass tube and reflectors, so is far *worse* a radiator than a perfect black body.

Q5

Using

$$\frac{\Delta Q}{\Delta t} = \frac{\Delta m}{\Delta l} c \Delta \theta$$

we get

$$(900 - 37) \, \text{J s}^{-1} = \frac{\Delta m}{\Delta t} 4200 \, \text{J kg}^{-1} \, \text{K}^{-1} \, 80 \, \text{K}$$

So the mass flow rate is

$$\frac{\Delta m}{\Delta t} = \frac{863 \, \text{J s}^{-1}}{4200 \, \text{J kg}^{-1} \, \text{K}^{-1} \times 80 \, \text{K}}$$

$$= 2.6 \times 10^{-3} \, \text{kg s}^{-1}$$

(to two significant figures)

We have assumed a perfect black body at a uniform 90°C, so our result is a lower limit.

Q6

The trough could be set up in a north–south orientation on an axis parallel to Earth's axis and driven to follow the Sun from east to west during the day.

Q7

Considering a full tube of water:

$$\text{mass} = \text{volume} \times \text{density}$$

$$= 1 \, \text{m} \times \pi (6 \times 10^{-3} \, \text{m})^2 \times 1000 \, \text{kg m}^{-3}$$

$$= 0.113 \, \text{kg}$$

Using $\Delta Q = mc\Delta\theta$

if t is the time (in seconds) taken to reach 100°C, then

$$(900-37)\,\text{W}\,t = 0.113\,\text{kg} \times 4200\,\text{J}\,\text{kg}^{-1}\,\text{K}^{-1} \times 90\,\text{K}$$

$$t = \frac{(0.113 \times 4200 \times 90)\,\text{J}}{863\,\text{W}}$$

$$= 50\,\text{s (to two significant figures)}$$

Q8

(a)

Total mirror surface area $= 70 \times 1.5\,\text{m}^2$

$$= 105\,\text{m}^2$$

Therefore

solar energy striking mirrors

$$= 600\,\text{W}\,\text{m}^{-2} \times 105\,\text{m}^2$$

$$= 6.30 \times 10^4\,\text{J}\,\text{s}^{-1}$$

(b) At 65% efficiency

energy supplied to target per second

$$= \frac{65}{100} \times 6.30 \times 10^4\,\text{J}\,\text{s}^{-1}$$

$$= 4.10 \times 10^4\,\text{J}\,\text{s}^{-1}\text{ (to three significant figures)}$$

(c) Using Stefan's law

$$P = \varepsilon \sigma A T^4$$

to find equilibrium temperature we get

$$T^4 = \frac{P}{\sigma A}$$

$$= \frac{4.10 \times 10^4\,\text{J}\,\text{s}^{-1}}{5.7 \times 10^{-8}\,\text{W}\,\text{m}^{-2}\,\text{K}^{-4} \times 1.5\,\text{m}^2}$$

$$= 0.4795 \times 10^{12}\,\text{K}^4$$

$$T = 0.832 \times 10^3\,\text{K}$$

$$= 8.3 \times 10^2\,\text{K (to two significant figures)}$$

Q9

$$\text{Tip speed ratio} = \frac{v_{\text{BG}}}{v_{\text{WG}}}$$

so

$$v_{\text{BG}} = \text{tip speed ratio} \times v_{\text{WG}}$$

$$= 7 \times 15\,\text{ms}^{-1}$$

$$= 105\,\text{ms}^{-1}$$

Q10

See Figure 8.15. Notice that α is the angle of attack of the aerofoil. Lift, L, and drag, D, will increase with increasing α until stalling occurs.

Q11

(a) Using Betz's equation

velocity at turbine

$$= \text{average of input and output speeds}$$

$$= \frac{v + \dfrac{v}{3}}{2}$$

$$= \frac{2}{3}v$$

(b)

Mass of air $=$ volume $\times$ density

$$= lA\rho$$

(c)

Distance travelled by air per second $= l = v$

(by definition)

l and v have the same numerical value (in SI units).

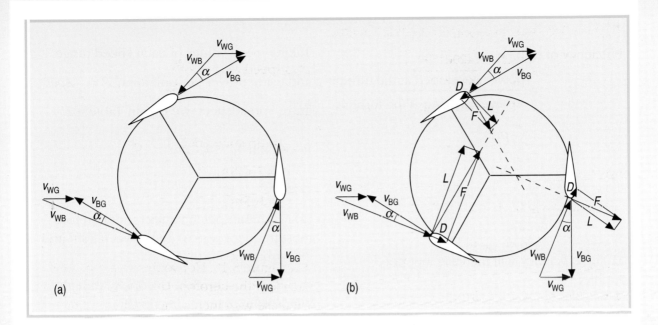

Figure 0.10 Answer to Question 10

(d)

$$E_k = \frac{1}{2} mv^2$$

and for the cylinder of air

mass = volume × density

$$m = lA\rho$$

so

$$E_k = \frac{1}{2} lA\rho v^2$$

Since l and v have the same numerical value

$$E_k = \frac{1}{2} A\rho v^3$$

But all this kinetic energy cannot be extracted from the wind because the air has to have some remaining energy to get it through and away from the turbine. If all the energy were extracted, the air would stop and would 'pile up' behind the turbine.

(e)

Mass of air passing through turbine per second

$$= \rho A \times \text{velocity at turbine}$$

$$= \frac{2}{3} \rho A v$$

(f)

Momentum change per second

$$= \text{mass} \times \text{velocity change}$$

$$= \frac{2}{3} \rho A v \left(v - \frac{v}{3} \right)$$

$$= \frac{4}{9} \rho A v^2$$

$$= \text{force of turbine}$$

(g)

Power developed = force × velocity at turbine

$$= \frac{4}{9} \rho A v^2 \times \frac{2}{3} v$$

$$= \frac{8}{27} \rho A v^3$$

(h)

Efficiency of turbine

$$= \frac{\text{power developed at the turbine}}{\text{power arriving at the turbine}}$$

$$= \frac{\frac{8}{27}\rho A v^3}{\frac{1}{2}\rho A v^3}$$

$$= \frac{16}{27}$$

$$= 0.59 \text{ or } 59\%$$

(i) The efficiency will increase, but not double.

Q12

$$P = \frac{1}{2}\rho A v^3$$

Density is expressed in kg m^{-3}, area is expressed in m^2, and velocity is expressed in m s^{-1}, so units of the right hand side of the equation are

$$\text{kg m}^{-3} \times \text{m}^2 \times \left(\text{m s}^{-1}\right)^3 = \text{kg m}^2\,\text{s}^{-3}$$

$$= \text{kg m s}^{-2} \times \text{m} \times \text{s}^{-1}$$

$$= \text{N m s}^{-1}$$

$$= \text{J s}^{-1}$$

$$= \text{W}$$

Q13

Taking mean values of each speed range, and using power per unit area, $P = \frac{1}{2}A\rho v^3$, and a spreadsheet, we obtain Table 8.2.

In column 4, $P = \frac{1}{2}\rho v^3$

Q14

(a) Maximum percentages (and therefore most frequent winds) lie between 200° and 280° from the north.

(b) They must be able to cope with high winds from several directions.

Q15

In the Pennines, the windspeed for most of the year is 2.5 m s^{-1}, so

$$P = \frac{1}{2}\rho A v^3$$

$$= 0.50 \times 1.3\,\text{kg m}^{-3} \times 1.0\,\text{m} \times \left(2.5\,\text{m s}^{-1}\right)^3$$

$$= 10.2\,\text{W}$$

Q16

In all cases, the term on the right-hand side must have the units of velocity, i.e. m s^{-1}, if the equation is to be valid.

Table 8.2

Speed range/m s^{-1}	Median speed, v/m s^{-1}	Frequency f/%	Power per unit area, P/W m^{-2}	$P \times \dfrac{f}{100}$ /W m^{-2}
0–1.4	0.7	15.2	0.223	(0.034)
1.4–3.2	2.3	24.3	7.908	1.92
3.2–5.4	4.3	30.0	51.680	15.50
5.4–8.0	6.7	18.0	195.496	35.19
8.0–10.6	9.3	2.3	522.832	12.03
		total over 100% of time (weighted sum) = 64.67		

For (a)

$$v = \frac{k\lambda}{g}$$

the units of the right-hand side are

$$\frac{m}{ms^{-2}} = s^2$$

so this cannot be correct.

For (b)

$$v = kg\lambda$$

the units of the right-hand side are

$$ms^{-2} \times m = m^2 s^{-2}$$

so this is also incorrect.

For (c)

$$v = k\sqrt{\lambda g}$$

the units of the right-hand side are

$$\sqrt{m^2 s^{-2}} = ms^{-1}$$

This equation has the correct units, but whether it is correct to include k (the dimensionless constant) cannot be verified by this method.

Q17

(a) E_{pot} available = $mg \times$ (mean height of water above low tide)

mass of water = density × volume

$$E_{pot} = 1.0 \times 10^3 \, kg \, m^{-3} \times \frac{15 \times 10^3 \, m \times 50 \times 10^3 \, m}{2}$$

$$\times 7.0 \, m \times 9.8 \, ms^{-2} \times \frac{7.0}{2} m$$

$$= 9.0 \times 10^{13} \, J \text{ (to two significant figures)}$$

(b) As the water is released, the tide is coming back in and rising, so the effective value of the mean height of the water above low tide falls. Also, we have the same problem as with the air turbine, i.e. if you take all the energy out then the water would stop moving and build up behind the barrage.

(c)

$$P = \frac{\text{work done}}{\text{time taken}}$$

$$= \frac{0.90 \times 9.0 \times 10^{13} \, J}{(5 \times 60 \times 60) \, s}$$

$$= 4.5 \, GW$$

Q18

(a)

Mass of water = density × volume

$$= 1.0 \times 10^3 \, kg \, m^{-3}$$

$$\times 7.0 \times 10^6 \, m^2 \times 96 \, m$$

$$= 6.72 \times 10^{11} \, kg$$

$$h = \left(750 + \frac{96}{2}\right) m$$

$$= 798 \, m$$

Potential energy stored in dam is

$$E_{pot} = mgh$$

$$= 6.72 \times 10^{11} \, kg \times 9.8 \, ms^{-2} \times 798 \, m$$

$$= 5.3 \times 10^{15} \, J \text{ (to two significant figures)}$$

(b)

Volume of water = $7.0 \times 10^6 \, m^2 \times 96 \, m$

$$= 6.72 \times 10^8 \, m^3$$

volume supplied in 1 second = $46 \, m^3$

power = energy supplied in 1 second

$$= \frac{5.3 \times 10^{15} \, J \times 46 \, m^3}{6.72 \times 10^8 \, m^3} s^{-1}$$

$$= 3.6 \times 10^8 \, J \, s^{-1}$$

(to two significant figures)

(c)

Duration of energy supply

$$= \frac{\text{total energy stored}}{\text{energy supplied per second}}$$

$$= \frac{5.3 \times 10^{15} \text{ J}}{3.6 \times 10^8 \text{ J s}^{-1}}$$

$$= 1.5 \times 10^7 \text{ s}$$

$$= 4100 \text{ h}$$

$$= 170 \text{ days}$$

(d) Volume supplied per second $= 46 \text{ m}^3 \text{ s}^{-1}$

radius of pipe $= 1.0$ m

cross-sectional area of pipe $= \pi r^2$

$$= \pi \text{ m}^2$$

length of column of water flow per second

$$= \frac{46 \text{ m}^3 \text{ s}^{-1}}{\pi \text{ m}^2}$$

$$= 14.6 \text{ m s}^{-1}$$

Therefore, mean linear fluid flow speed is 15 m s^{-1} (to two significant figures).

Q19

Power of each turbogenerator

$$= \frac{0.40}{2} \times 1.1 \text{ kg m}^{-3} \times \pi \left(50 \text{ m}\right)^2 \times \left(5 \text{ m s}^{-1}\right)^3$$

$$= 2.16 \times 10^5 \text{ kW}$$

Total output $= 0.25 \times 40000 \times 2.16 \times 10^5 \text{ W}$

$$= 2 \text{ GW}$$

(to one significant figure)

Q20

Taking the approximate value of 1000 kW h m^{-2} yr^{-1} and efficiency of 0.75

national output

$$= 24 \times 10^6 \times 16 \text{ m}^2 \times 1000 \text{ kW h m}^{-2} \text{ yr}^{-1} \times 0.75$$

$$= 2.88 \times 10^{11} \text{ kW h yr}^{-1}$$

$$= 33 \text{ GW}$$

So, a devolved solar programme could supply impressive amounts of thermal energy.

In this section, we are going to test the accuracy of engineering models of heat supply and loss by comparing calculated heat demand for your home with what you were billed for. We will also look at ways to reduce your bills and try to find explanations for discrepancies.

You will need the following:

- One year's worth of energy bills for your home.
- Climatic data for your area from a local library or the Meteorological Office. (As an example we have supplied climatic data for southeast England in Table 9.8 in Appendix 9.1.)
- A plan of your house, showing sizes of walls, floors, ceilings, glazed areas, and the type of materials used in the construction. Work to nearest 10 cm for windows, doors and room sizes. Calculate the volumes of each space and the areas of the doors and windows. (If you don't live in a house or bungalow, it may be easier to share data with another member of your group, as the analysis of mobile homes and flats, for example, will be a little more difficult for you to do.) If you live in a terrace or a semi, the party walls (those shared with a neighbour) can be discounted when calculating heat loss – after all, they probably heat their houses to about the same temperature as you heat yours.
- Estimates (arrived at by experiment if necessary) of water consumption and temperature.
- A record of the thermostat settings in your home if you have central heating, and the period during which the heating is run (the heating season).
- Details of the occupancy of your home (that is, the number of people in your household and how many hours a day/week each of them is in the house.

Actual energy consumption

(a) Calculate your household's energy consumption for the year from your energy bills. If you use electricity and gas this should be fairly straightforward and should give an answer in kilowatt hours (kW h). You should convert this to joules. If you use oil, solid fuel (such as coal), gas or wood, use the values for calorific value given in Table 9.7 in Appendix 9.1 to determine the energy consumed. Take care not to include stockpiled fuel, such as oil stored in tanks, or wood on the wood pile.

(b) Make a measurement of the rising main water temperature from the cold water tap in the kitchen. (This really ought to be averaged over the whole year, but that is not possible for this short project.)

(c) Find the mean outside temperature for the heating season (e.g. October to April). You can use the data in Table 9.8 in Appendix 9.1 if you live in the southeast of England, otherwise you will need to obtain your own climatic data.

Copy and complete Table 9.1.

Table 9.1

Energy consumed per year from electricity/J
Energy consumed per year from gas/J
Energy consumed per year from oil/J
Energy consumed per year from solid fuel/J
Energy consumed per year from wood/J
Energy consumed per year from solar power/J
Total I/J
Rising main water temperature/°C
Mean outside temperature during heating season/°C
Mean inside temperature during heating season/°C
Heating season duration/s

9.1 Estimating consumption

 What is energy used for in your home?

Energy in the home is used primarily for four activities:

- water heating
- heating the air you ventilate your home with
- replacing the heat lost through the fabric of your home (wall, roofs, etc.)
- running appliances.

Water heating

This is the most straightforward to deal with. Estimate the amount of water consumed in each of the activities in Table 9.2, the temperature at which this is done, and the number of times per week each is done. You can measure flow rates easily using a measuring jug and a watch – from these you will be able to determine the contents of the bath or water consumed in a shower more easily. Remember that 1 litre of water has an approximate mass of 1 kg. Manufacturers' instructions, *Which?* reports and local water, electricity and gas showrooms and helplines may help you.

Copy and fill in Table 9.2. (*Note:* **Specific heat capacity** of water, $c = 4200 \, \text{J kg}^{-1} \, \text{K}^{-1}$ and energy consumed in heating it, $\Delta Q = mc\Delta\theta$.)

Do not use mercury in glass thermometers in an occupied bath or shower.

Table 9.2

Activity	No. per week	No. per year	Volume of each/litre	Volume per year/litre yr^{-1}	Temperature of water used in activity/°C	Energy consumed per year/J yr^{-1}
Bathing						
Using a sink						
Showering						
Using a dishwasher						
Using a washing machine						
					Total II	

Air changes

Air changes cause energy transfer because the warm stale air that leaves the home (whether intentionally or not) is replaced by fresh cool air, which then has to be brought up to a comfortable temperature. Recommended air changes per hour are shown in Table 9.3. Using the volumes of your rooms from your survey, and the mean outside temperature from your own data in Table 9.1, complete Table 9.3. (*Note*: The heating season may be rather less than 12 months. Density of air = 1.29 kg m^{-3} at standard temperature and pressure. Take the specific heat capacity of air as 1000 J kg^{-1} K^{-1}.)

Table 9.3

Room	Changes per hour	Changes per year	Volume	Volume displaced per year/m^3 yr^{-1}	Energy consumed per year/J yr^{-1}
Kitchen and bathrooms	3				
Living rooms	2				
Bedrooms	1				
				Total III	

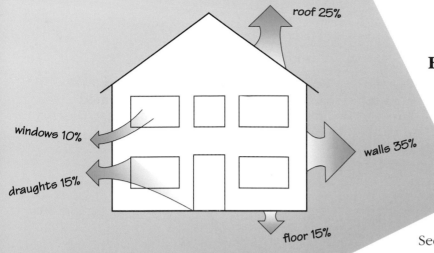

Figure 9.1
Thermal energy
losses (%) by
various routes from a
house with little or
no insulation

Fabric losses

Figure 9.1 shows the main routes through which thermal energy escapes from our homes.

However, to estimate how much energy is lost through the fabric of your home, we must define a new term, the **U-value** (which you actually met in Section 8.1 on solar panels, although we didn't name it there.)

The U-value for an interface such as a window, wall, floor or roof is defined as the rate of flow of thermal energy through the interface, per unit area, per unit temperature difference. In other words, it is the energy that would flow through one square metre if a temperature difference of one kelvin existed across the interface. The units for U-values are W m^{-2} K^{-1}.

$$\frac{\Delta Q}{\Delta t} = AU\left(\theta_{in} - \theta_{out}\right) \qquad (9.1)$$

Where $\dfrac{\Delta Q}{\Delta t}$ is the rate of thermal energy flow in watts, A is the area of the interface through which thermal energy is flowing, θ_{in} is the inside temperature, θ_{out} is the outside temperature, and U is the U-value. If energy is flowing through several interfaces in parallel – for example, through walls and windows let into the walls – these expressions can simply be added together (the symbol Σ means 'sum'). The temperature difference also can be taken out as a factor giving

$$\frac{\Delta Q}{\Delta t} = \left(\theta_{in} - \theta_{out}\right)\Sigma\,AU$$

U-values are closely related to thermal resistance, R, given by a thermal analogy to Ohm's law. In Ohm's law, the initiator of charge flow is the potential difference:

potential difference = rate of flow of charge × resistance

or

$$\Delta V = \left(\frac{dQ}{dt}\right)R$$

In the thermal analogy, the initiator of thermal energy flow is the temperature difference.

Temperature difference = rate of flow of thermal energy
× thermal resistance

or

$$\left(\theta_{in} - \theta_{out}\right) = \frac{dQ}{dt}R$$

(Remember Q is charge above, but thermal energy here.) The units of R are K W^{-1} and temperature is in kelvin.

Comparing this with the definition of U-value in Equation (9.1) reveals that

$$AU = \frac{1}{R}$$

for a single interface and

$$\Sigma AU = \frac{1}{R'}$$

where R' is the thermal resistance of the building as a whole.

What if you don't know the U-value of a certain interface? If you know what it is made of, the U value can be calculated from thermal conductivities. Again, to understand thermal conductivities, an electrical analogy helps:

$$R = \frac{\rho l}{A}$$

where l is the length, A the cross sectional area and ρ the resistivity of a conductor.

$$\rho = \frac{1}{k}$$

where k is the conductivity, so

$$R = \frac{l}{kA}$$

This is true for thermal resistances too if k this time is the thermal resistance.

 What are the units of k?

$$\text{Units}\left(k\right) = \text{units}\left(\frac{l}{RA}\right)$$

$$= \frac{m}{K\,W^{-1}\,m^2}$$

$$= W\,K^{-1}\,m^{-1}$$

Remember

$$AU = \frac{1}{R}$$

so

$$U = \frac{1}{RA}$$

$$= \frac{k}{l}$$

For a simple interface

$$U = \frac{k}{l}$$

For more complex interfaces, made up of layers, add the thermal resistances then find U from

$$U = \frac{1}{A\sum R}$$

The air layer either side of an interface contributes greatly to $\sum R$ and so reduces U.

Worked example: finding U from first principles

Suppose a cavity wall, plastered on the inside, is composed of materials as shown in Figure 9.2. We will first calculate R for each part (or look it up in Table 9.9a in Appendix 9.1), then $\sum R$, then $U = \dfrac{1}{A\sum R}$.

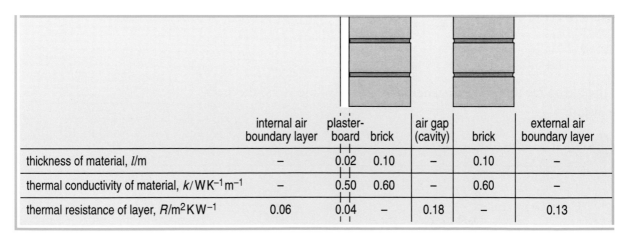

	internal air boundary layer	plaster-board	brick	air gap (cavity)	brick	external air boundary layer
thickness of material, l/m	–	0.02	0.10	–	0.10	–
thermal conductivity of material, k/WK^{-1}m^{-1}	–	0.50	0.60	–	0.60	–
thermal resistance of layer, R/m^{2}KW^{-1}	0.06	0.04	–	0.18	–	0.13

Figure 9.2
Construction of a typical cavity wall

Then we must complete the last row of data for brick using $R = \dfrac{l}{kA}$ (R is quoted for boundary layers and cavities as shown in Figure 9.2). For each brick layer

$$R = \frac{l}{Ak}$$

$$= \frac{0.10\,\text{m}}{1\,\text{m}^2 \times 0.60\,\text{W}\,\text{K}^{-1}\,\text{m}^{-1}}$$

$$= 0.17\,\text{K}\,\text{W}^{-1}$$

Since U is defined for one square metre we can put $A = 1\,\text{m}^2$ in the

equation $U = \dfrac{1}{A\Sigma R}$ to give

$$U = \frac{1}{1\,\text{m}^2 \Sigma R}$$

$$= \frac{1}{\Sigma R}\,\text{m}^{-2}$$

$$= \frac{1\,\text{m}^{-2}}{\left(0.06 + 0.04 + 0.17 + 0.18 + 0.17 + 0.13\right)\text{K}\,\text{W}^{-1}}$$

$$= 1.33\,\text{W}\,\text{m}^{-2}\,\text{K}^{-1}$$

In your initial survey you wrote down the types of materials used in the construction of your house. Calculate the U-values for each material. Table 9.9 in Appendix 9.1 will help you. Copy and fill in Table 9.4.

Table 9.4

Interface description	Area, A/m^2	U-value/ $\text{W}\,\text{m}^{-2}\,\text{K}^{-1}$	$AU/\text{W}\,\text{K}^{-1}$	Loss through interface per year/J yr^{-1}
Walls				
Roof				
Floors				
Windows				
	$\Sigma AU =$			Total IV
	Total thermal resistance, $R = [1/(\Sigma AU)]/\text{K}\,\text{W}^{-1}$			

Bills comparison

Now total your three annual heating components (Totals II, III and IV) and compare this with the total from your bills in Table 9.1 (Total I).

Are they close? Give an answer in percentage terms and comment on any similarities or differences.

calculated demand (Totals II, III and IV)   =

energy supplied (Total I)   =

percentage difference   =

 Why have we not included the energy consumed by appliances such as the TV in our survey?

Because these ultimately produce thermal energy which offsets heating. There are other 'free' energy sources too. See Figure 9.3.

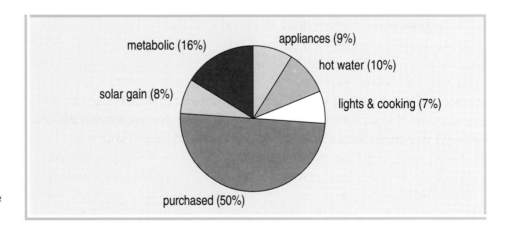

Figure 9.3
Sources of energy for domestic space heating

Only half of our heating demand is paid for and supplied directly. Some comes from losses in the water heating system, some from the Sun, some from waste heat from appliances and some from our own bodies.

9.2 Making savings

Most of our homes are ventilated in a rather haphazard way through cracks and open windows, and much thermal energy is lost when waste water from baths, showers and other appliances leaves the house. A more controlled ventilation and drainage system in the home could employ **heat exchangers** to transfer outgoing energy from stale air and waste water to incoming air and clean water at an efficiency of about 80% (thus cutting air and water heating bills to a fifth of their original cost).

Such systems are actually available in DIY centres for about £500 and can be installed for a similar sum; however, because people change homes

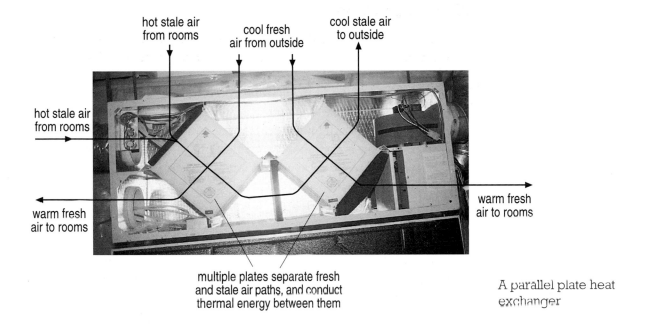

hot stale air from rooms

cool fresh air from outside

cool stale air to outside

hot stale air from rooms

warm fresh air to rooms

warm fresh air to rooms

multiple plates separate fresh and stale air paths, and conduct thermal energy between them

A parallel plate heat exchanger

fairly frequently, investment in such devices is not often attractive. (Tax payers used to be given tax relief on home improvement loans in the UK, and the costs were free of VAT – perhaps these concessions should have remained on projects that resulted in long-term savings of fuel.) Energy efficient homes do cost more to buy – about £2000 at current prices – but can save more than £200 a year in fuel bills. Barretts, the home builders, estimate that super-insulated buildings incorporating sophisticated controls cost about £780/m^2 to build as opposed to £670 for orthodox buildings. Social Services provide as much as £300 000 000 per year in heating subsidies to people who are old, infirm or poor – the very people who are most likely to be living in severely under-insulated homes.

Heat loss through the roof can be reduced by using fibre **insulation**, 30 cm is now the recommended thickness for this. Walls can also be insulated by spraying foam or mineral fibre into the cavity between the two layers of brick or blocks used to build the walls of most modern houses.

Double-glazing can reduce heat losses through the windows, by trapping an insulating layer of air between the layers of glass. The optimum gap between the glass panes for good thermal insulation is about 20 mm but noise reduction needs a bigger cavity. Recently developed coatings applied to the panes set up a kind of greenhouse effect, which also reduces heat losses. Nevertheless the U-value for well-insulated windows still exceeds 2.5 W m^{-2} K^{-1} and if you compare this figure with the U-values you used for Table 9.4 you can see that it is still quite high. Double-glazing ranks low on home owners' priority lists unless frame replacement is needed or noise is a problem.

If you have solid masonry walls any extra insulation must be placed on the interior or exterior of the walls: which is the most sensible and why?

This is a tricky one. If insulation is put on the inside, the heating system won't have to heat the walls themselves so the room can be heated quickly with little cost. But the room will also cool quickly as soon as the air is changed for ventilation. If insulation is external, the walls will have to be heated initially as well as the air in the room. This will take time and large amounts of energy the first time, but the walls will take a long time to cool. When the air is changed, the cool fresh air will quickly gain warmth from the walls. The choice depends on the occupancy of the house: if people are in all day, and the heating is permanently on, exterior insulation is probably best, if the house is unoccupied for large parts of the day and the heating is off, internal insulation is best.

Using the U-values from Table 9.9(c) in Appendix 9.1, calculate potential savings of energy and cash that could be made by installing, for example, double-glazing, or cavity wall, loft or external insulation and re-do Table 9.4 to give a new total – Total IV(a).

Alternative supplies

All houses collect solar energy – you may have identified passive **solar gain** as a reason for any disparity between your billed consumption and calculated consumption – but good design can enhance winter solar gain while limiting overheating in summer.

Suggest how you could achieve this.

You could include several south facing windows and few north facing ones. Overhanging eaves give shade in the summer but let the winter low-altitude rays into the building. Deciduous trees can also offer shade in the summer and let in low rays during the winter.

Suppose your house faces southwest, with 10 m^2 of window facing southwest, 3 m^2 facing southeast and northeast, and 4 m^2 facing northwest. (Southwest and southeast mean 45° to south.) The northwest and northeast windows capture very little radiation in the Northern Hemisphere. From Table 9.10 in Appendix 9.1, one square metre at 45° to south and at 0° to vertical captures approximately 622.5 kW h m^{-2} yr^{-1} (taking the mean of 40° and 50° values), so 13 m^2 will capture 622.5 kW h m^{-2} yr^{-1} × 13 m^2 = 8092.5 kW h yr^{-1}.

Q1 Using the values given in Table 9.10 in Appendix 9.1, estimate the energy 'capture' of the windows in your home. ◆

In reality, a lot of the light will be reflected (especially at low angles of incidence) or absorbed and re-radiated outwards by the glazing, so your answer will be an upper estimate.

Does this account for the disparity between billed consumption and calculated consumption?

Unless your home is very modern or is a 'solar house' designed to capture solar energy by its shape, glazing, awnings, orientation and insulation, you will most likely have to consider *active* not *passive* energy capture, for example using solar panels (thermal and voltaic), windmills, etc. Using Tables 9.8 and 9.10, try to decide if solar water heating and solar and wind electricity generation could supply most of the rest of your energy needs. There is a further problem – look at weather data in Tables 9.8 and 9.10.

Office building at the Open University campus showing overhanging eves

? What difficulties can you see in exploiting energy capture by wind and Sun?

The solar regime favours summer collection, while the wind regime favours winter collection. So you could have a glut of hot water in the summer and a surplus of electricity in the winter.

Of course, if wind power could provide heat while solar power provided air conditioning, this might be resolved; the technologies do exist. (A bonus is that U-values are higher in windy conditions so wind powered heat is an excellent idea!) This way it would be possible to have sufficient generating plant to supply energy needs during minimum demand, buying in energy to top it up as necessary *or* you could have sufficient generating plant to provide for maximum needs, selling surplus energy elsewhere during periods of lower consumption (this is perfectly feasible with electricity, though it can only be sold on at relatively low prices).

Exploration 9.1 Using a blender as a kettle: or how windmills could produce thermal energy

Apparatus:

◆ kitchen blender or food processor   ◆ thermometer
◆ measuring jug or balance

> *Do not run blender with fingers or a thermometer in the jug or grinder housing. Do not run the blender for longer than the instructions specify.*

Place a small amount of cold water (sufficient to cover the rotor blades) in the blender jug or food processor and measure its temperature. Switch the blender on and run it for about a minute. Switch off, wait for the blades to stop rotating, and then measure the water temperature again. Record the temperature rise and the mass of water heated, and then calculate the increase in thermal energy of the water. (Specific heat capacity of water $c \approx 4200 \ \text{J kg}^{-1} \ {}^{\circ}\text{C}^{-1}$.)

 Where did the thermal energy come from?

Work done on the water is manifested by an increase in its thermal energy.

Such a device scaled up could convert wind power directly into thermal energy.

(*Note:* (a) Joule and Rumford performed similar experiments – in Joule's case falling weights did the work in a celebrated experiment called 'the mechanical equivalent of heat'. (This is described on page 133 of the SLIPP unit *Physics on the Move*.) Today, we would see this as determining *c*. Unfortunately, we can't quantify the work done in our experiment very easily. (b) Aircraft carrier arrester hook cables drive a similar water heating device to dissipate the energy; in this case, apparently, the water boils!)

Heat pumps

Another way of producing heat from mechanical energy is by using a **heat pump**.

Fridges use heat pumps to cool the interior and release thermal energy from the back of the fridge. If you stood your fridge in the doorway and opened the fridge door to the outside, thermal energy would be extracted from the outside and deposited in your kitchen.

 What would be the drawback of this air to air heat pump?

The doorway would be blocked and the fridge would soon ice up! (You could of course place the fridge against next door's house and suck the heat out of their home into yours – but they might wonder why ice was forming on their wallpaper, and this wouldn't solve the energy crisis, because their thermostat will kick in more often!)

 So, what is the solution?

Use the ground, a solar panel and/or stale water as the cold source
or don't cool the evaporator (the cold pipes inside the fridge) as
much.

Carnot's equation applies to fridges and heat pumps too, in a slightly
modified form.

First, though, the efficiency, or **coefficient of performance** (CoP), for a
fridge is defined slightly differently from how we have defined efficiency
before. After all, the objective here is to extract energy, hence
CoP = Q_{cold}/W, where Q_{cold} is energy absorbed and W is work needed to
extract and discharge this thermal energy. For a heat pump, the objective
is to supply as much Q_{hot} as possible for minimum work done. Here
CoP = Q_{hot}/W. (You met efficiency in Section 2.2.) So, for a heat engine

$$\varepsilon = \frac{W_{out}}{energy_{in}}$$

$$= \frac{T_{high} - T_{low}}{T_{high}}$$

for maximum (Carnot) efficiency.

For a heat pump

$$CoP = \frac{Q_{hot}}{work\ in}$$

$$= \frac{T_{high}}{T_{high} - T_{low}}$$

And for a fridge

$$CoP = \frac{Q_{cold}}{work\ in}$$

$$= \frac{T_{low}}{T_{high} - T_{low}}$$

 Is your waste water energy sufficient to provide your space heating
needs using a heat exchanger? Look at Tables 9.2, 9.3 and 9.4.

Possibly not, but it can be cooled to below its inlet temperature by
the heat pump, thus providing a larger value of Q_{cold}, but with the
heat pump operating at slightly lower efficiency.

A heat pump can reclaim waste heat while providing space or even water
heating for your home. Unfortunately, they are expensive and

complicated, and, until recently, employed **CFCs** – potent greenhouse gases and harmful to the ozone layer if they leak.

'Minichips', micro-CHP or (μCHP)

As you learnt in Section 3, minichips are miniature cogeneration or combined heat and power units. Since they provide electricity and thermal energy, they need to be matched to demand, or too much electricity may be produced, which is sold at a loss, or too much heat is produced, which must be got rid of, or else the plant runs at lower than capacity or maximum efficiency. Usually, thermal energy output is matched to demand and extra electricity bought in – not least because summer demand for space heating can be zero.

Q2   Match a minichip installation from Table 9.5 to your electricity demand. Will the heat output match your water demand? ◆

Table 9.5 Typical manufacturer's performance figures for minichip units

Name of unit	Make	Engine capacity/ litre	Gas input/ kW	Thermal energy output*/ kW	Power/ kW
TOTEM	Fiat	0.90	60	38	15
CG100	Leyland	2.25	62.5	38	15
CG200	Ford	6.20	163	86	45
Mini CHP	Waukesha	3.60	107	59	26
Mini CHP	Waukesha	13.30	338	180	90
NUTEC	MAN	20.90	463	260	155

* The output only includes thermal energy from water at about 85°C; some engines supply 'low-grade' heat at around 30°C.

Q3   Now match a minichip to water heating demand – will the electricity it produces exceed your demand? ◆

Of course, excess energy can be used for space heating too. Output can be maximized by driving a heat pump with a minichip.

Conclusion

Round off your audit by copying and completing Table 9.6 and commenting on the prudence of any remedial work or investment you recommend.

Table 9.6

Current UK per capita domestic consumption from Section 2	_____
Current per capita domestic consumption in your household	_____
Current consumption per unit area recommended in your style of home	____ ____
Current domestic consumption per unit area in your household	_____

Achievements

After working through this section you should be able to:

- evaluate thermal energy transfer through materials
- use U-values to evaluate the thermal performance of buildings
- predict the effect of wind on a building's thermal energy demands
- understand some heat recovery techniques using heat pumps and heat exchangers
- evaluate the value of double-glazing.

Glossary

CFCs Chlorofluorocarbons. Synthetic chemicals used as propellants in aerosol cans, for refrigeration and as foaming agents. They are considered to be a contributing factor in the destruction of the ozone layer and can remain in the atmosphere for more than 100 years. Production has been phased out, but an illegal trade still exists.

Coefficient of performance The ratio of useful energy or work (or power) output to total energy or work (or power) input for a device. Expressed as a fraction or a percentage.

Heat exchanger A device for transferring energy from a fluid at a high temperature to a fluid at a lower temperature without the fluids coming into contact with each other. It can be employed to make use of 'waste' heat or to maximize efficiency of a process.

Heat pump A device used for heating that takes thermal energy, Q, from some part of the environment, such as the air, soil or water, and supplies it to a working substance. An electric motor or engine does work, W, on the substance in a cycle that results in the emission of thermal energy ($W + Q$) into the space to be heated (which is at a higher temperature than the heat source). It functions in a similar way to a refrigerator.

Insulation A material that reduces the transmission of heat from a body.

Solar gain Heat input to building due entirely to the Sun shining on windows and other surfaces.

Specific heat capacity Unit: joule per kilogram per kelvin ($J\ kg^{-1}\ K^{-1}$). The energy required to raise the temperature of unit mass of a substance by 1 K.

U-value Unit: watt per square metre per kelvin ($W\ m^{-2}\ K^{-1}$). The rate of flow of thermal energy through an interface, per unit area, per unit temperature difference, i.e. the heat that would flow through one square metre if a temperature difference of one degree existed across the interface.

Answers to questions in the text

Q1

The answer depends on the number of windows in your home and their orientation.

Q2

It will probably exceed it.

Q3

Probably not, going by national figures.

Appendix 9.1
Useful data

Table 9.7

Fuel	Density/kg m^{-3} (approx.)	Calorific value
Coal	2300	30.6 MJ kg^{-1}
Oil	680	43.2 MJ kg^{-1}
Gas	0.60	38.0 MJ m^{-3}

Table 9.8 Meteorological Office data for southeast England

	JAN	FEB	MAR	APR	MAY	JUN	JULY	AUG	SEPT	OCT	NOV	DEC	YEAR
Temperature/°C 1941–70													
Average daily mean	3.1	3.4	5.5	8.4	11.3	14.5	16.1	15.7	13.7	10.5	6.3	4.1	9.4
Average sunshine/hours 1941–70													
Monthly	51.9	69.7	116.3	160.6	202.1	215.8	200.7	184.3	137.9	103.1	63.3	47.8	1553.5
Daily mean	1.67	2.49	3.75	5.35	6.52	7.19	6.47	5.95	4.60	3.33	2.11	1.54	4.26
Windspeed/m s^{-1} for 1978, 10 m above ground													
	4.1	4.2	4.0	4.1	3.7	3.6	3.4	3.1	3.3	3.3	3.4	3.8	

Table 9.9(a) Thermal properties of building and insulating materials

Description	Thermal conductivity, k/ $W K^{-1} m^{-1}$	Thermal resistance, R/$K m^2 W^{-1}$
Gypsum or plasterboard		
10 mm		0.057
13 mm		0.078
Plywood	0.12	
Hardwood/particle board	0.14	
Carpet underlay		0.144
Carpet and fibrous pad		0.367
Carpet and rubber pad		0.217
Tile – asphalt, linoleum, vinyl or rubber		0.009
Glass-fibre	0.036	
Mineral fibre with resin binder	0.042	
Lightweight aggregates including		
expanded shale, clay, or slate;	0.75	
expanded slags;	0.52	
cinders;	0.36	
pumice, vermiculite;	0.17	
also cellular concretes	0.10	
(all usually used for unit construction, high-rise developments)		
Sand, gravel or stone	1.73	
Brick, common	0.72	
Brick, face	1.30	
Concrete blocks		
100 mm		0.13
200 mm		0.20
300 mm		0.23
External render: lightweight aggregate on metal lath (20 mm)		0.083
Maple, oak and similar hardwoods (20 mm)	0.159	
Fir, pine, and similar softwoods (20 mm)	0.115	
Aluminium (20 mm)	221.5	
Steel, mild (20 mm)	45.3	
Steel, stainless (20 mm)	15.6	

Table 9.9(b) Some common values of surface resistance coefficients

	Surface resistance coefficient/$m^2 K W^{-1}$
Internal wall or window	0.13
External wall or window	0.06
External roof	0.05
Internal floor ceiling (upward energy flow)	0.11
Internal floor ceiling (downward energy flow)	0.15

Table 9.9(c) U-values for various kinds of construction

(i) External walls: masonry

Type of construction	Thickness/mm	U-value/W $m^{-2} K^{-1}$
Brickwork		
1 Solid walls, unplastered	105	3.3
	220	2.3
	335	1.7
2 Solid wall, with 16 mm plaster on inside face		
(a) with dense plaster	105	3.0
	220	2.1
	335	1.7
(b) with lightweight plaster	105	2.5
	220	1.9
	335	1.5
3 Solid wall, with 10 mm plasterboard lining fixed to brickwork plaster dabs	105	2.8
	220	2.0
	335	1.6
4 Cavity wall (unventilated) with 105 mm outer and inner leaves with 16 mm plaster on inside face		
(a) with dense plaster	260	1.5
(b) with lightweight plaster	260	1.3
5 As 4, but with 230 mm outer leaf and 105 mm inner leaf		
(a) with dense plaster	375	1.2
(b) with lightweight plaster	375	1.1
Brickwork/lightweight concrete block		
6 Cavity wall (unventilated) with 105 mm brick outer leaf, 100 mm lightweight concrete block inner leaf with 16 mm dense plaster on inside face	260	0.96
7 As 6, but with 13 mm expanded polystyrene board in cavity		0.70
Lightweight concrete block		
8 Solid wall, 150 mm aerated concrete block, with tile hanging externally and with 16 mm plaster on inside face		0.97
9 Cavity wall (unventilated) with 75 mm aerated concrete block outer leaf, rendered externally, 100 mm aerated concrete block inner leaf with 16 mm plaster on inside face, 50 mm cavity		0.84

(ii) External walls: framed construction

Type of construction	U-value/ W m^{-2}K^{-1}
1 Tile hanging on timber battens and framing with 10 mm plasterboard lining, 50 mm glass-fibre insulation in the cavity and building paper (assumed 10% area of glass-fibre bridged by timber)	0.65

(iii) Flat roofs

Type of construction	U-value/ W m^{-2}K^{-1}
1 Asphalt 19 mm thick or felt/bitumen layers on solid concrete 150 mm thick (treated as exposed)	3.4
2 As 1, but with 50 mm lightweight concrete screed and 16 mm plaster ceiling	2.2
3 As 2, but with screen laid to falls, average 100 mm thick	1.8
4 Asphalt 19 mm thick or felt/bitumen layers on 150 mm thick autoclaved aerated concrete roof-slabs with slight slope	0.88

(iv) Pitched roofs (35° slope)

Type of construction	U-value/ W m^{-2}K^{-1}
1 Tiles on battens, roofing felt and rafters, with roof space and aluminium foil-backed 10 mm plasterboard ceiling on joists	1.5
2 As 1, but with boarding on rafters	1.3
3 As 2, but with 50 mm glass-fibre insulation between joists	0.50
4 As 3, but with 100 mm glass-fibre insulation	0.35

(v) Windows

Window type	Percentage of area occupied by frame	U-values for stated exposure level/ W m^{-2}K^{-1}		
		Sheltered	Normal	Severe
Single-glazing				
wood frame	30	3.8	4.3	5.0
metal frame	20	5.0	5.6	6.7
Double-glazing				
wood frame	30	2.3	2.5	2.7
metal frame with thermal break	20	3.0	3.2	3.5

Sheltered: low-rise buildings or the lower floors of the buildings in urban areas (windspeed, $v = 1$ m s^{-1}).
Normal: 4th to 8th floors of buildings in urban areas ($v = 3$ m s^{-1}).
Severe: upper floors or buildings on exposed sites ($v = 9$ m s^{-1}).

Table 9.10 Solar energy impinging on 1 m^2 at various orientations with average cloud cover

		Solar energy/kW h yr^{-1}									
Angle	90°	580	600	640	680	720	760	840	900	950	930
of	80°	595	660	680	720	760	790	850	890	930	930
surface	70°	600	690	730	760	790	860	900	930	950	930
to	60°	610	690	760	810	855	900	940	960	950	930
south	50°	620	700	790	835	890	935	980	990	980	930
	40°	625	720	790	870	930	990	1000	1000	990	930
	30°	630	730	820	910	970	1010	1020	1020	990	930
	20°	635	740	840	925	1000	1030	1040	1030	980	930
	10°	640	770	870	940	1050	1050	1060	1050	1000	930
	0°	645	780	880	960	1050	1050	1060	1050	1000	930
		0°	10°	20°	30°	40°	50°	60°	70°	80°	90°
					Angle of surface to vertical						

The Royal Society in the UK and the US National Academy of Sciences joined together in June 1997 to produce a document called 'Towards sustainable consumption'. In this they quote the following statement written by 58 experts who came together to consider the issue of continued population growth and the effect of this on the environment:

> Resource use, waste production and environmental degradation are accelerated by population growth. They are further exacerbated by consumption habits, certain technological developments and particular patterns of social organisation and resource management … Scientists, engineers and health professionals should study and provide advice on transitions to economies that provide increased human welfare with less consumption of energy and materials.
>
> ('Towards sustainable consumption', Royal Society and US National Academy of Sciences, June 1997)

After you have studied this SLIPP unit, we hope that you will understand the statement above and appreciate the issues raised by the unit. You should be aware of the complexity of the issues we have introduced you to and know that making changes in one area is unlikely to provide a solution to all the problems affecting environment.

At the time of writing (autumn 1997), the targets set at the 1992 Earth Summit in Rio were in the news. At this summit it was agreed that by the year 2000, CO_2 emissions should be no higher than 1990 levels. In the UK, CO_2 emissions are expected to be lower in the year 2000 than they were in 1990. However, the UK, Russia and Germany are the only countries from the world's top ten emitters who are predicting that they will meet the target (Hawley, 1996). The USA and Australia, for example, are unable to meet the 2000 deadline – the USA wants to extend its deadline to the year 2012.

Energy consumption has increased 22-fold since 1952, and over the next 25 years the per capita energy consumption in developing nations, such as China, is likely to increase by 85%. But even at this new level, a typical Chinese person's consumption will be less than 20% of an average American's consumption today (Hawley, 1996, p. 92).

The population of Bangladesh is increasing by about 2.4 million per year, while that of Britain is increasing by about 100 000 per year. Yet, because CO_2 emissions per person in Britain are 50 times higher than in Bangladesh, 100 000 people in Britain cause more than twice the CO_2 emissions of 2.4 million people in Bangladesh (Royal Society, 1997).

Demand for cars continues to increase – in the UK an additional 5233 cars are registered every day, and the USA now has more cars than drivers. You may like to do some project work focusing on the problems caused by the ever-increasing number of cars on the road and suggest some

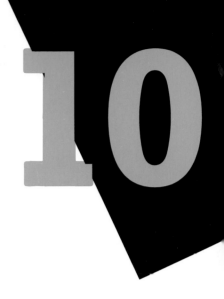

potential solutions. The 'Further reading and resources' section contains details of some information that may start you off.

The Royal Society and the US National Academy of Science have defined a research and action agenda to identify critical factors and priorities to encourage the development of a sustainable environment. Their agenda includes:

- vigorous research on sustainable energy sources and on energy efficiency in all its forms, and vigorous promotion of those technologies for energy efficiency that already exist
- development and diffusion of environmental technologies
- research on ways of defining and determining environmental costs, and on incorporating them into pricing and taxation policies
- improvement of energy- and land-efficiency of food production
- management, protection and regeneration of natural systems
- minimization, recycling of materials and of components
- development of new and replacement materials.

(Royal Society, 1996, p.3)

Bearing in mind what you have learnt from this unit, do you agree with their agenda? Can you add to it?

If you think back to the beginning of this unit, you will realize what a lot of physics you have covered by looking at the environment from the perspective of energy and transport.

To help you to appreciate how far you have come, look back through the list of achievements for each section. If you feel unsure about any of them, go over the relevant section(s) of this unit again. When you feel fairly confident about most of these achievements ask your teacher for the exit test for this unit. When you have done the test, consult your teacher, who has the answers and will probably wish to go through them with you.

We hope you have enjoyed learning about the physics of the environment with this supported learning unit, and that you want to use more units in the series.

Further reading and resources

Aird, A. (1972) *The Automotive Nightmare*. Arrow Books, London.

ASE (1981) *Science in Society: Teacher's Guide*. Heinemann Education Books, London.

BP Review of World Gas (1991) August.

BP Statistical Review of World Energy (1991) June.

BP Statistical Review of World Energy (1996) (incorporating the BP *Review of World Gas*).

British Association for the Advancement of Sciences (BAAS) (1996) 'Roads: the way ahead', *Visions for the Future Report 2*, Report of DTI Conference in May 1996, pp. 1–8.

Cambell, R., Holgarth, S, and Miller, R, (eds) (1991) *Teaching and Learning about the Environment*, Packs 1–3.

Capener, P., Houghton, T., Sage, J., Goodier, A., Holeman, H., Preece, L. and Williams, J. (1995) *Science with Technology Materials*: 'Green buildings'; 'Cars and the environment'; 'Energy in Kalyanpura: investigating energy and development issues'; 'Making use of renewable energy'; 'Evaluating environmental impact'.

Chapple, M. and Environmental Physics Group (1995) *Earth and Atmosphere*. Institute of Physics, London.

De Circco, J. and Ross, M. (1994) 'Improving automotive efficiency', *Scientific American*, December, pp. 30–5.

De Circco, J. and Ross, M. (1994) 'The amateur scientist: measuring the energy drain on your car', *Scientific American*, December, pp. 78–9.

Department of Energy (1987) *Energy Across the Curriculum: a resource directory for GCSE*. Energy Efficiency Office, London.

Department of the Environment (1996) *Energy Management*, November/ December.

Department of the Environment (1996) *The Environment in your Pocket*. Government Statistical Service, London

Department of Trade a Industry (n.d.) *Renewable Energy: a resource for Key Stages 3 and 4*. Renewable Energy Enquiries Bureau, Harwell.

Energy and Environmental Management (1997) 'Taking the message home', July/August, pp. 10–11.

Energy Efficiency Office (1992) *Best Practice Programme – Good Practice Guide: Introduction to Large-scale Combined Heat and Power*. Department of the Environment, London.

Energy Efficiency Office (n.d.) *Building on Success*. Department of the Environment, London.

Foley, G. (1976) *The Energy Question*. Pelican, London.

Hamer, M. (1996) 'No respite from city smogs', *New Scientist*, 6 April, p. 5.

Hawley, R. (1996) 'Urban energy needs and the environment', *Engineering Science and Education Journal,* April, pp. 89–95.

Jain, P. K. (1991) 'On blackbody radiation', *Physics Education,* vol. 26, pp. 190–4.

Lothian Energy Group (n.d.) *Living with Energy.* Department of Energy, London.

Meadows, D. H., Meadows, D. L., Randers, J. and Behrens, W.W. III (n.d.) 'The limits to growth', a report for the Club of Rome's project on the predicament of mankind.

Meadows, D. H., Meadows, D. L., Randers, J. (1992) *Beyond the Limits: global collapse or a sustainable future.* Earthscan Publications, London.

Patterson, W. C. (1976) *Nuclear Power with a New Postscript.* Pelican, London.

Pearce, D., Markandya, A., Barbler, E. B. (n.d.) *Blueprint for a Green Economy.* HED.

Pearce, F. (1997) 'Greenhouse wars', *New Scientist,* 19 July, pp. 38–43.

Rackett, S. (1996) 'Taken for £100bn ride', *Railwatch,* vol. 69, October.

Ross, S. (1991) 'Physics in the global greenhouse', *Physics Education,* vol. 26, pp. 175–81.

Royal Society and US National Academy of Sciences (1997) 'Towards sustainable consumption', *Councils of the Royal Society and the National Academy of Sciences,* June (copies obtainable from The Royal Society, 6 Carlton House Terrace, London SE1Y 5AG. Tel: 171 839 5561; email: ezmb013@mailbox.ulcc.ac.uk).

SATIS Project (1990) *Earth and Environmental Science.* SATIS Resource Material, Association for Science Education, Hatfield.

Scientific American Special Issues: *Managing Planet Earth* (September 1989); *Energy for Planet Earth* (September 1990). ABB Asea Brown Boveri Ltd.

Shell Briefing Service (1994) *Renewable Energy,* no. 1.

Szokolay, S. V. (1977) *Solar Energy and Building* (2nd edn). Architectural Press, London, Halsted Press Division, John Wiley, New York.

Understanding Electricity. Education Catalogue Resources for Schools and Colleges (1997).

Vale, B and Vale, R. (1976) *The Autonomous House: design and planning for self-sufficiency.* Thames and Hudson, London.

Waste Watch (n.d.) *Wise Up to Waste: a cross-curricular resource for 15–18 year old secondary students.* Sponsored by Coca-Cola Great Britain.

Useful contacts

British Airways coordinates the 'Visions for the Future' scheme, which brings together 16–25-year-olds to discuss issues and prepare published reports. Contact: Natasha Martineau, Visions for the Future, BAAS, 23

Savile Row, London SW1X 2NB. Tel: 0171 973 3051; e-mail: ba.visions@mcr1.poptel.org.uk

Centre for Alternative Technology, Llwyngwern Quarry, Machynllech, Powys, Wales. A weekend field trip can be built around this site (accommodation and wholefood available), which is close to Ironbridge (Museum and YHA) and a nuclear power station.

CREATE – Centre for Research, Education and Training in Energy, Kenley House, 25 Bridgeman Terrace, Wigan, WN1 1TD; web site www.create.org.uk; e-mail: info@create.org.uk

Stirling engines (some solar powered) are obtainable from: Solar Engines, PO Box 15625, Phoenix, AZ 85060, USA.

Acknowledgements

Grateful acknowledgement is made to the following sources for permission to reproduce material in this unit:

Photographs and figures

Cover photo: Malcolm Parry; p. 48: A thermal power station – *Guardian*/Denis Thorpe; p. 50: Tomatoes growing at Drax B – National Power Picture Unit; p. 51: Battersea power station – CEGB Information Services; p. 61: Model T Ford – Popperfoto; p. 68 Urban smog – Hartmut Schwarzbach/Still Pictures; p. 77: Ford Taurus – *Environmental Science and Technology*, vol. 25, p. 1191, 1991, © Ford Motor Company; p. 77: A solar car – Mark Baker/Popperfoto; p. 79: Smokey Mountain in Manila – Richard Skelding; p. 93: The Aachen vehicle – *Ford Highlights*, vol. 3, no. 4, p. 3, Figure 3, © Ford Motor Company; p. 94: Peugeot 106 – Peugeot; p. 95: Figure 5.3 – *Ford Highlights*, vol. 3, no. 4, p. 5, Figure 8, © Ford Motor Company; p. 100: Figure 5.8 – *Ford Highlights*, vol. 1, no. 2, p. 7, Figure 2, © Ford Motor Company; p. 108: Bike culture – *Bike Culture Quarterly*/David Eccles; p. 118: Robert Bunsen – S. Muspratt, *Chemistry, theoretical, practical, analytical* (1853); p. 136: A solar house – Malcolm Parry; p. 165: Solar furnace used for high-temperature research at Odeilo, France – Liz Whitelegg; p. 168: Energy from sugar cane – ETSU (top right photo); p. 169: A silicon photovoltaic cell – Open University; p. 175: Vertical axis wind turbines – Derek Taylor/Altechnica; A horizontal axis wind turbine – Mike Anderson/Renewable Energy Systems; p. 177: A sail windmill – A. J. Coulson; p. 178: Heavy blades being lifted into position on a wind turbine at Grandpa's Knob, USA; p. 184: Salter's duck – ETSU (top photos)/Open University (bottom photo); p. 185: Oscillating air column on Islay – ETSU; p. 186: Tidal barrage near St Malo, France – ETSU; A medieval style tidemill – Nigel Smith; p. 188: A hydroelectric power station on the River Tay at Pitlochry, Scotland – J. Allan Cash Ltd; p. 189: A pump storage scheme at Cruachan, Scotland – Eric Thorburn/Glasgow Picture Library; p. 191: Geysers – Popperfoto; p. 211: A parallel plate heat exchanger – Seattle Film Works; p. 213: Office building at the Open University campus showing overhanging eves – Liz Whitelegg.

Magazine article

pp. 147–51: 'The greenhouse effect', *New Scientist*, no. 92, 6 July 1996.

The authors and Management Group would also like to thank Linda Doyle, Sahab Fawanah, Steve Goddard, Rosemary Gray, Peter Hughes and David Tawney for their helpful comments and advice.

Index